THE COMPULSIVE OVEREATER

The Compulsive Overeater

Seven Steps to Thin Sanity

by GEORGE F. CHRISTIANS

Doubleday & Company, Inc.
GARDEN CITY, NEW YORK
1978

ISBN: 0-385-14038-x

Library of Congress Catalog Card Number 77–90808

This book is fondly dedicated to Dr. Frank, an alcoholic who saved my life; to Marianne, a compulsive overeater who answered her telephone; to my wife, who loved me beyond measure, no matter how insane I had become; and to members of Overeaters Anonymous all over the world.

"God grant us the serenity to accept the things we cannot change; the courage to change the things we can; and the wisdom to know the difference."

Foreword

In the bewildering maze of contradictions and myths that surround obesity, I can find only two truths: no one really understands what obesity is; and physicians such as myself have been unsuccessful, singularly so, in its treatment.

In a simple sense, obesity can be defined as weighing more than the average for one's sex, age, height, and body structure. This state of obesity can be further categorized as mild, moderate, or gross, depending on the degree to which the patient deviates from the accepted standards of normality. Such people are sometimes euphemistically called "portly," "pudgy," "fat," or "roly-poly": derogatory descriptions that conventional society chooses to identify its overweight members.

The medical complications of pathological obesity are legion and well known. These include hypertension and other cardiovascular diseases; diabetes mellitus; gallstones; varicose veins; and flat feet and a variety of other musculoskeletal abnormalities. Obese people are also known to be more than usually accident-prone and to incur greater risks when undergoing surgical procedures than do their thinner peers. This list is far from being inclusive. Insurance actuarial tables heartily attest to the odor in which they hold the obese, and the increased premiums are but an additional forfeit for being fat.

The immediate precipitating cause of obesity seems straightforward enough: the obese eat too much food or do not take enough exercise to compensate for the amount of energy they consume in calories. What seemingly eludes everyone, however, is *why* some people eat more than they need, and, equally important, how to combat this tendency toward compulsive overeating. Some have postulated that the fat were overfed in infancy; that they have more or larger fat cells than normal people; or that they have genetic predispositions toward an obese condition. The solutions offered are equally varied, as this book by George Christians points out, and are generally useless to the sufferer from pathological compulsive overeating. Dieting, whether under a physician's tutelage or not, is seldom successful. Diet pills do little except, perhaps, make the patient *feel* better about his eating. Various dieting associations and unorthodox medical "clinics" seem to offer little that is more than fleetingly helpful to the overeater in his attempt to control what I believe to be an obsession.

This book you are about to read offers another alternative that I sincerely feel has great merit. Much of what the author has to say is derived from the philosophy of a fellowship that has rescued many thousands from the terrible addiction of alcohol. It seems eminently sensible that the methods of Alcoholics Anonymous can be applied to the problems of the compulsive overeater. As in the case of obesity, alcoholism seems to defy and baffle the medical practitioner.

Lastly, the author of *The Compulsive Overeater* has been

startlingly frank in his description of how miserable it feels to be fat. I think he has made a brave, honest, and very forthright attempt to communicate with his fellow obese patients and explain their frustrations in the thin world they live in. This is a book that compulsive overeaters can strongly identify with, one that will help them gain insight into a common problem. After reading this, they should feel less alone and more understood. It needed to be written and it should help a lot of unfortunate people.

—"Dr. Frank"

THE COMPULSIVE OVEREATER

ONE
ooooóoooooo

I am a compulsive overeater. I am powerless over food. Like drug addicts, sexual deviates, kleptomaniacs, and a host of other afflicted, I have a compulsion—overeating—that has harmed my career, shamed my family, and damaged my health beyond any hope of complete recovery. Yet I have hope. I write in order to share what I have learned with other compulsive overeaters, and their families, friends, and employers, and to offer them hope as well.

After fifty years of hysterical alternation between starvation dieting and gross overfeeding, I have found a measure of sanity. What I was like before and what I have become are part of this book. A substantial portion is derived from the experiences of others, all compulsive overeaters, members of Overeaters Anonymous, who, in the best traditions of that organization, wish to preserve their anonymity.

I weigh about 185 pounds, am slightly over six feet tall, have a large skeleton, and medically am no more than 5 or 6 pounds overweight. But to get here, over fifty-three years, I have gained more than 750 pounds! My present weight is the same as my football weight as a high school sophomore (I weighed more as a freshman), the same as during my military years on the Italian front in World War II, and the *least* I have weighed since. (I mustered out of the army at 218.)

Two years ago, at the height of my insanity, I was a 276-pound drunk with hypertension (blood pressure 210/170) and diabetes (sugar 445). I sweated constantly. My tongue was cracked (from diabetes). I coughed and wheezed, unable to sleep at night or catch a decent breath by day. If I was medically critical, psychiatrically I was paranoid and severely schizophrenic. My only friends were my children, my loving, thin wife, and my doctor: a gentle, good man who told me to leave his office and die on my own.

"I'll not sign your death certificate," Dr. Frank told me. "Find yourself a quack to do it."

I live only three blocks from the Pacific Ocean and a beach I was ashamed to be seen on—I and my rolls of fat, my great boobies like a cow's. My wardrobe was down to one greasy, stained pair of size-50 pants (the only ones I could button) and three horrible synthetic shirts from the "Big Guys" store. I wore moccasins and loafers because I could not bend to tie my shoes. My body was wracked by muscle cramps because my frame rebelled against the load it carried. Exercise, to build the muscles, was as life-threatening as the fat. The circle was vicious. All the food I could cram in my stomach, five or six martinis before dinner to kill the pain in my head, the alcohol increasing my already senseless appetite and cutting my self-control even further—these were my defenses against the frustration, the anger, the self-pity and self-hate.

I really did think about killing myself. There was a gun in

the closet, a .357 magnum. I looked at it, thought about it. I became obsessed with one particular knife on my desk, a little X-Acto-type thing with a cunning, sharp blade. How I stared at that blade. But I went on. I would let the food, the alcohol, the hypertension, and the diabetes do the job for me.

What was the nature of this strange, baffling compulsion that was killing me? Why was I a freak? Especially I, who thought I was so superior. Why was it that every time I tried to diet—with all the resolve and will power in the world, with the love and best wishes of my loved ones behind me—this thing, this obscene *thing*, would reach out and return me, kicking and screaming, to the fat man I really was? My obsession over food was as terrible a monster as anything ever conjured by the literature of psychiatry *and it was killing me.*

The beginning of my slow return to sanity was the realization that I was insane and my compulsive addiction to food was my disease. After fifty years, this was the beginning of the road back. I was—I am—and I ever shall be, to my life's last breath, a compulsive overeater.

Like the alcoholic, I had been lying to myself about food, lying to my doctors, lying to my family, and lying to my employers. I had bad glands, water retention, lousy genetics, strange fat cells; I gained weight "on nothing at all"; I was low in thyroid; I didn't get enough exercise; and so on, and so on. It was all a crock. I was a cheating, lying compulsive overeater who sneaked food on the side, gorged food, hid food in secret places, and sometimes didn't even know I had eaten food five minutes later. *I was like an alcoholic.*

And as with alcoholism, there is no cure for compulsive overeating.

In fact, compulsive overeating, in a strange way, is worse than alcoholism. Both will kill you. Both mark you. Both cause people to turn away from you. Both break up homes and both ruin your chances for decent employment. But unlike alcohol, food is essential to us all.

If you, or a member of your family, are an alcoholic, with all the terrible implications of that dread word, you may laugh at a whip-cream junkie. But, fat or thin, we all must eat. Needle freaks don't need fixes any more than alcoholics really need booze to survive. But if you are a sober alcoholic, you just try eating lunch every day in a saloon. Try looking at those bottles on the counter and see how you maintain your sobriety. Every restaurant, every cafeteria, every McDonald's is my neighborhood saloon, advertising the product that's killing me. Every supermarket is my bottle shop.

I told Dr. Frank, "You are putting an alcoholic on a diet of three small Bourbons a day."

And Dr. Frank is himself an alcoholic. He stared at me, shuddering.

"My God. I couldn't drink a diet of drinks. It would kill me. In six months I'd be dead."

With that, things began to happen. The wheels in our brains began to mesh. It was the beginning: the first day of the rest of my life. How I have managed to regain my sobriety, my sanity, and refrain from compulsive overeating is the story this book has for you if you, too, are a compulsive overeater, or your wife, husband, child, or best friend is.

The medical profession (except for Dr. Frank) failed me as it fails other compulsive overeaters. Medicine fails because it follows a rigid model of scientific inquiry unchanged since the first struggling birth of the scientific method.

Psychiatry fails us because it, too, follows the medical/scientific model of "disease." Faddish pop clinics, pop diets, and behaviorist psychologists fail us. Authoritarian techniques fail

4

us; they smack more of cause than cure. Anybody who charges us a fee fails us, because there is no love in profit.

All else failing, a few of us have banded together in little groups, like the alcoholics of forty years ago, to work our own recovery. By so doing, we have discovered sanity and a higher authority than science. If you are a compulsive overeater, we hope and pray you will find your sanity, too. But whatever means we have found and whatever sanity may have returned illuminate one fundamental truth: we remain compulsive overeaters, however thin, for all the rest of our lives.

Here is what I have found and this is how it works.

Compulsive overeaters are people who eat compulsively. If you are of a Freudian bent, you might say they have an oral fixation, although this doesn't seem to mean much, at least to me. I think compulsive overeating is a method people develop *as children* to alleviate pain and frustration—as an antidote to anger perhaps—and carry forward into adulthood for reasons they cannot understand.

The human race has always celebrated its happy times by feasting. For primitive people an abundance of game was the signal for glutting to satiation. Anthropological films seem to bear this out. Important times of the year in religious terms were—and are—feast days. Thanksgiving Day, Christmas, and Easter are American glutting days. Fourth of July is incomplete without a picnic. Birthdays, especially for children, are major feast days. Birthday cake and ice cream (and the bigger the portions the better) are important social/parental encouragements for the child ("Be happy—eat!").

6

Eating attitudes tend to be cultural. The Jewish mother is a cultural stereotype ("Eat—it's good for you!"). When the Mafia decides to eliminate a prominent member, tradition holds he be killed on a full stomach. The German, Swede, or other North European cannot imagine Christmas without a house filled with the pleasant smell of cookies. My father was born in a small German-American town in southern Wisconsin. No funeral was complete without a "smear": a feast prepared by the ladies of the Lutheran church to be consumed after the interment. My eldest daughter married into an Armenian family, and her Armenian wedding feast, painstakingly and lovingly prepared by the mother and father of the bridegroom and myriad relatives, was magnificent—and incredibly caloric.

I grew up during the depression years ("Eat—millions of poor people are starving!"). No sin, in my Wasp home, exceeded that of wasting food. If I fell and skinned my elbow, I didn't get love and kisses; I got candy or a leftover piece of pie. The happiest moments of my childhood involved food: lots and lots of good food. An angel food cake with chocolate frosting was a temple, to be approached with awe and proper salivation ("Eat—what's the matter, isn't it any good!"). You *respected* food. To leave crumbs on the plate was to show lack of respect for the cook ("Eat—don't you love Mommy?").

Food was a reward for a job well done. Getting a good report card was a signal for a special food treat . . . or, better yet, an evening out in a restaurant. In the firm I worked for, a good business year was always celebrated with a glutting party. When my outfit returned home from Europe after the war, we were embraced by doughnuts at the dock and all the steak, pie, and milk we could hold as soon as we arrived at the mess hall. How is a Girl or Boy Scout honors' night celebrated?—by a banquet, of course, the same way we celebrate any act of merit or heroism ("Eat—you certainly deserve it!").

Many—maybe most—children overeat. The majority, however, never become significantly obese, but live out their lives as normal thins. Why, then, do a small proportion of children overeat compulsively and continue this pattern throughout adulthood? Why do they diet, lose huge amounts of weight, only to revert to former eating habits once again?

When we have a desire to do something and are prevented from doing it by forces beyond our control, the result is frustration. Frustration is a destructive force. We spin around, inside our head, like a top out of control. We seek outlets for our frustration. Some people are able to tolerate frustration. Others are not. Outlets for frustration are many: brooding and fits of depression; physical substitution or sublimation such as athletics, taking cold showers, reading a book, twiddling your thumbs; anger, hostility, or other antisocial behavior; or engaging in a strange, unique (to you) kind of behavior we call *compulsion*.

Compulsive behavior is irrational in the sense that it makes no sense, either to you or to others. It is "escape-valve behavior." Some types of compulsive/obsessive behavior win social praise; others do not. The "workaholic" who spends sixteen hours or more a day building his business and making vast amounts of money is an American culture hero (although not necessarily to his wife or his physician). But the individual who compulsively chases members of the opposite sex or exposes himself to small girls in schoolyards, who compulsively steals useless items from stores, who drinks to excess or eats to excess, is compulsive in either an antisocial or an antipersonal way. Or both. The obsessive/compulsive person is venting

8

frustration in a way he or she cannot understand, cannot account for, and cannot deal with. *The devil made me do it.* I once knew a man who was having severe marital problems, although neither he nor his wife wanted to divorce for family and religious reasons. This man would come home from work in the evening, sit down at a table, and play endless games of solitaire until the wee hours of the morning, speaking hardly a word to his wife or children. He was, of course, venting his anger and frustration in a compulsive way, but probably not in a manner society would see as unduly alarming.

How a childhood compulsion to seek love and approval becomes obsessive behavior in later life is difficult if not impossible to answer. Suffice it that every single compulsive overeater I have ever listened to tells a story almost identical to my own experience. We were rather solitary, withdrawn children with a high degree of perceived frustration who overate compulsively, became fat, became more frustrated and lonely because we were fat, and continued to overeat because we were already fat and frustrated. So we live lives of quiet desperation, trapped in bodies we hate, repelled and repulsed by a society dominated by thins. Like Peeping Toms, child molesters, kleptomaniacs, and alcoholics, we fat compulsive overeaters are victims of a strange compulsion we cannot understand or handle. Why do we eat? "The devil makes us do it!" It's as good an answer as any.

THREE

○○○○○○○○○○○○○○○○

I knew (in the way one knows things one does not quite believe) that I was considered pretty and that even my big ass was considered attractive by some, but I loathed every extra ounce of fat. It had been a lifelong struggle: gaining weight, losing it, gaining it back with interest. Every extra ounce was proof of my own weakness and sloth and self-indulgence. Every extra ounce proved how right I was to loath myself, how vile and disgusting I was. Extra flesh was connected with sex—that much I knew. At fourteen, when I had starved myself down to ninety-eight pounds, it was out of guilt about sex. Even after I had lost all the weight I wanted to lose—and *more*—I would deny myself water. I wanted to feel *empty*.

—Erica Jong, *Fear of Flying*

We may or may not live in a world of uncertainty, a world of future shock, or whatever fanciful phrase has been allotted our generation this past week. But this I know: we live in the world of thin. If your cardiologist is king of this new world, Twiggy is queen. And Erica Jong may be lonely, but not alone.

The sexually oriented ads in the Los Angeles *Free Press* and others of that sort are quite specific: "No fats, please." Skinny sex is in. And compulsive overeaters are out.

We are in what psychologists and sociologists call a classic double-bind, a situation in which you are given a choice of two equal alternatives . . . either of which is calamitous. Damned if you do and damned if you don't.

Let me illustrate. You are taken to dinner by a wonderful man at a very famous and expensive French restaurant. Your dream man tells you to order whatever pleases you from the menu. He is showing you his love. You may order whatever you wish. Price is no object. He insists you finish with at least one delectable little pastry stuffed with cream, chocolate, and calories. And after the dinner is over, dreamboat takes you to his apartment. To make love. To a thin girl. You are first loved by being overfed fat and then sexually adored because you are thin. The dinner and the aftermath are a double-bind.

Remember Sunday dinner at Granny's house? Dear old Granny, bless her heart.

"Lord, I don't know what's happening to that child. He/she has gained so much weight. I can't imagine why that child is so fat. Of course, fat always did seem to run in the family."

But you've already guessed what Granny served for Sunday dinner. And how she expected you to eat every last morsel, every speck of fried chicken, mashed potatoes, and gravy, how she insisted you belong to the clean-plate club. How *hurt* she was if you pecked at your food.

"My, how that child loves my food. One more piece of my chocolate cake couldn't possibly hurt, now could it. And be sure to take some home with you."

11

Granny was the essence of the double-bind.

I suspect, strongly, that this kind of childhood double-bind is the beginning of the insanity of compulsive overeating. Children eat because eating well pleases their parents. But becoming fat displeases their parents. Mother love and mother food become all mixed up.

Sunday night was, for me, the happiest night of the week. My father was never a friendly, really loving man. To tell you the truth, he frightened me more than a little. He disapproved of virtually everything I did. He told me how inept I was around guests in our home, how I failed to shake hands properly, failed to smile properly, failed to "look them in the eye" as we met. That I was fat and nonathletic saddened him (as it did me) and my lack of normal boy-acting ability, my bookishness, my (to him) acts of just plain cowardly behavior sickened him, and he let me know, often, how he felt.

But Sunday night we were "buddies." Sunday night was a ritual event. Father would go to the drugstore for ice cream, chocolate sauce, and whipped cream. He and I would raid the kitchen—together—and make great mounds of peanut butter on toast sandwiches, or grilled cheese with bacon sandwiches. He and I would gorge ourselves sick. And I loved Sunday evening with Father. It was that rare moment when the two of us were doing something together we really enjoyed: compulsively overeating.

And Monday I would be told I was too fat.

My parents were gone a lot, on vacations and trips, leaving my brothers and sister and me behind to be watched over by the family maid. And that maid, by the way, was one hell of a cook. The more lonely I became, the more I raided the pantry. I can never remember a time when a pie or a cake wasn't around somewhere. As I think about it, I guess I tried to eat myself out of loneliness. I also learned one very, very bad habit: to eat while reading. I can read a book—eat—and never know I've eaten. *That* is a very bad habit.

Any situation that places an individual in a double-bind produces anxiety. As the anxiety level increases, we try to cope by introducing a mode of behavior from the past that has been effective. Such tension-reduction mechanisms might include the excessive use of alcohol, sexual relief, overworking compulsively, withdrawal (taking to one's bed, for example), use of tranquilizers or stimulants, savage misuse of an automobile (and perhaps a fatal accident), taking dope, inner- or outer-directed anger, or compulsive overeating.

A *neurosis* (or neurotic behavior) is basically a way of reacting to an anxiety-productive situation in an antisocial manner that neither the actor nor those around the actor understand, appreciate, or can tolerate. You don't know why you are doing what you are doing; neither do those around you understand your "strange" behavior: therefore your neurotic act makes waves, so to speak. You are acting "nutty"—neurotic.

People who exhibit neurotic behavior are more than likely to lose friends and support from those around them. The consequences for the actor are severe: guilt, shame, and paranoia set in. This, of course, raises the anxiety level, and the neurotic act is repeated.

That is what I mean when I talk about my "insanity" of compulsive overeating.

(Excessive *undereating*—physicians call it *anorexia*—is also a neurotic compulsion and a reaction to guilt-productive double-bind situations; it is most common among young girls of high school or college age. The individual deliberately starves herself—sometimes to death. Anorexia and compulsive overeating behavior have much in common, along with alcoholism and drug abuse, certain forms of sexual neurotic behavior, and other antisocial reactions to guilt and anxiety. The quotation from Erica Jong's *Fear of Flying* at the beginning of this chapter is a classic anorexic statement.)

Boys get in double-binds because they are expected to eat every last bit of motherly-love food set in front of them—and then be thin, lithe, athletic boys. Mother food and mother love get all mixed up somehow.

But boys have a con game they can play with themselves. Growing up, for boys, is growing big. And growing big is often regarded, at least for a time, as a positive good. Dad is "big." The moose men who play professional football are "big."

As good old Granny says, "My . . . isn't he a big boy!"

So boys can indulge themselves, to some extent at least, in the self-delusion that fat is "big." (My boyhood hero was a football player named Bronko Nagurski, a moose man and all-American from Minnesota who eventually starred with the Chicago Bears. What I wanted was to be as "big" as Bronko.)

But at the onset of puberty that delusion begins to crumble into self-shame and self-hate. Suddenly . . . suddenly a desirable self-image is a muscular torso, a narrow waist, speed, agility, and, most important of all, a large penis. As puberty begins, boys begin to look at one another in a different way. And the fat boy in the locker room with his penis buried in rolls of fat is at least as hateful, or doubtful, a self-image as the flat-chested girl in a high school suddenly seemingly filled with jiggling breasts.

Boys are frightfully cruel at a certain age. They begin to grow those hoses. And the kid with the biggest prick in the locker room may in fact *be* the biggest prick in the school, but he damned well isn't ashamed of *that*.

I point this out to say to girls that you aren't the only

sufferers in the world. Fat boys have their own little problem. And the little problem is, at least for the moment, the biggest little problem in the world. "Being big" has taken on a new meaning.

But girls are probably in a worse double-bind than boys. To the extent mother love is loving Mother's food ("Eat it because I made this especially for you . . . because I love you") the young girl learns to be fat. Mother's affection and Mother's cooking gets all mixed up. Mother loves her because she loves Mother's cooking. Cooking "something special" is, for Mother, an act of loving sacrifice.

Time after time I have heard obese men and women say that their mothers seldom if ever showed affection by hugging or kissing or by praise for little acts well done. The cooking—the food—was the love and the reward Mother gave her son or daughter. And not to reciprocate, not to love and devour Mother's food down to the very last morsel, not to come back for seconds, *was hating Mother.*

But the other side of the double-bind was this: "If you don't lose weight, if you stay fat, no decent boy will ever marry you. No boy in his right mind would ever take you out looking so fat!"

"If you don't eat my cooking after I've slaved to make this over a hot stove all day . . . I'll hate you!"

"If you don't get thin, you won't get a decent husband. You won't get a decent sex life. And if you don't get thin and get a decent husband, I'll hate you!"

And you're damned if you do and damned if you don't. Hang your clothes on a hickory limb, but don't go near the water.

(A sicker problem than this—and unfortunately a rather common one—is the thin, good-looking mother who deliber-

ately fattens up her daughter, then tells the child she is "ugly."
The story of Snow White may be a classic working out of
this particular double-bind. "Mirror, mirror on the wall
. . . who is fairest of them all?" So she gives the kid a hunk of
chocolate cake poisoned with calories.)

I don't honestly know if compulsive overeating causes sexual maladjustment or if sexual hang-ups cause compulsive
overeating. It is probably one of those chicken-or-the-egg-
coming-first things. But one fact comes out loud and clear in
therapy rap sessions among compulsive overeaters: they have
sexual problems.

What seems to come out is this:

I am fat. Therefore I am a bad person. Because I am a bad
person, I am not the kind of man or woman a *good* person
would have sex with.

Therefore: if you have sex with me, either you are lying
when you say you love me, or else you are a vile pervert who
enjoys having sex with fat people.

Some men who are compulsive overeaters seek out the
favors of prostitutes (vile women) because good (normal)
women couldn't possibly love "vile" them. Or else they become somewhat neuter or simply masturbate (doing a "vile
thing" with vile themselves).

Compulsively overeating girls seem to do much the same:
either living an overly promiscuous life with "vile" men, or
else forgoing sex entirely.

One girl in our group (call her Barbara) is married, has four
children, is substantially overweight, and is the victim of a particularly vicious double-bind. Her husband expects her to
cook his favorite meals, expects her to drink with him (he is
an alcoholic), and then refuses to have sex with his wife because she is "too fat." (She puts up with this situation because

of the children, because of her Catholic faith, and because she is masochistic—as are many, many compulsive overeaters.)

Fat and guilt are ham-and-egg twins. Fat people who are compulsive overeaters probably suffer more from the guilts than most others do, with the possible exception of alcoholics who fall into the same compulsive pattern. When I was a fat kid I got hooked on guilt, and being hooked on guilt is to be the victim of a destructive force that tears you apart.

For instance, next week I plan to be on a river in Oregon for the opening day of the trout season up there, waving my rod, line, and fly back and forth as deftly as possible, doing what brings me as much pleasure as anything I can conceive of doing. And if I should be fortunate enough to hook a fish, I shall keep only those my friends and I need for the frying pan, returning the others to the water as carefully as I can, with wet hands, and removing the tiny, barbless hooks I use with stainless-steel forceps I conned from a physician friend for that purpose.

But in order to take this trip which will give me such great pleasure, I must leave my wife, Betty, to the mundane house-work she naturally detests, spend money I might otherwise spend on the two of us together, and be utterly selfish. (I have just yesterday made certain purchases—a new reel, line, and some flies—and will do my utmost to conceal these from my wife. I know this is silly. I know she wants me to take the fishing trip. And yet I feel guilty. I have a lifetime of feeling guilty, am well practiced in guilt.)

Many or most men I know do a certain amount of fishing, golfing, hunting, or even an occasional bit of whoring around without the guilts I've got.

I even wonder if I'll look "right" on that trout stream. Will I look *Field and Stream* enough to pass? Or *fat?* God help me,

I feel more apprehension about looking thin enough on that trout stream than about abandoning Betty to the pots and pans.

Fat guilt! Like Mount Everest . . . it's there. Always something to feel guilty about. We compulsive overeaters are surely the biggest masochists in the world.

I'm always trying to *please* people, to do the *right* thing. I worry about looking fat: ergo, it seems, I have learned to worry about everything else too and feel guilty about everything.

As Americans, we lead our lives in a world communicated to us by media undreamed of by our ancestors: primarily a world of pictures on television and motion picture screens, of photographs, rather than the simple print media of years ago. My childhood reading included Robin Hood, for example, and his famous villainous friend the Sheriff of Nottingham. It might be, although I disremember, that the sheriff was described as "stout" or even "fat." I forget. I forget primarily because print descriptions didn't really convey the idea of "fat" as loathsome. There were fat kings like Old King Cole, I guess; jolly Saint Nick whose tummy shook like a bowl full of jelly, of course; even kindly and well-meaning nitwits like Dickens' Mr. Micawber . . . but no "fat slobs."

The fat slob, male or female, is a rather recent invention of the advertising man, the National Heart Association, the internist, the psychologist, the diet-book writer, and, of course, the writers of diet articles in *Redbook* and *Cosmopolitan*. (We also have *Esquire* and *Playboy* and *Penthouse* to frighten flat-chested little girls with color spreads of pneumatic breasts and, just lately, *Playgirl* and *Viva* to terrorize men with photographs of pneumatic cocks.)

Forget the Sheriff of Nottingham. Remember the southern sheriff on TV a few years back—fat and mean? Nasty? Fat and nasty? Could you imagine that sheriff going to bed with Twiggy?

The center of the matter is this: we live in a world that, for better or worse, defines thin as good and fat as hateful.

If you are fat, you are going to hate yourself because you are a member of the society doing the definitions. And if you are fat, you are going to be guilty and anxiety-ridden, and you are going to do something, anything, to rid yourself of that anxiety. Pray God what you do isn't overeating compulsively.

I even feel guilty about Annie, a smallish female fox terrier who lives in our home and occupies the sofa when my back is turned. Annie, not being able to read magazines or watch TV, has turned herself into a compulsive overeater of cheese, choice ends of roast beef, cookies, and other undoglike foods. Like any child who mistakes food for affection, Annie is becoming quite stout. And, God help me, I did it to her because I feed her things I wouldn't feed myself . . . not any more.

Fat guilt is an endless circle. Because I feel guilty, I eat because eating somehow kills the pain. And because I have overeaten compulsively, I feel guilt. So I overeat. Round and round. And rounder I go.

Maybe I could accept the fact that obesity is medically dangerous. (As Buddhists say, "After ninety-nine years all things die.") But I cannot accept the guilt and self-hate of obesity because these are more destructive than corroded arteries or faulty insulin production, which can be somewhat contained by medicine, at least for a time. But the guilt gets me. I know of no magic pill that will reduce my suit size or make me love myself in the mirror. And even if there were such a pill, becoming an amphetamine freak isn't the answer I'm looking for.

The fundamental fact about compulsive overeating and the

obesity it produces is the effect these have on your head—on the way you regard your self. Since I have started communicating my feelings to other compulsive overeaters I have learned certain truths: everyone feels guilty about being fat; everyone wants to be a thin, trim man or woman; everyone wants a normal, sane sex life. Everyone wants thin sanity.

Last night a girl named Vivian attended one of our local meetings of Overeaters Anonymous. "Vivian" comes from a nearby city and she had this to say:

"I'm an alcoholic, a pill freak, I've shot dope with a needle, and I'm a certified schizophrenic . . . and I'll say this: fat broads are the most fucked-up people in the whole world."

Well, Vivian, I've got news for you. Men—fat men—are just as fucked-up. For every fat girl dying of shame and loneliness there is a fat man.

I think it's time we got together and talked it over.

FOUR
ooooooooooooo

ARE YOU A COMPULSIVE OVEREATER?

		YES	NO
1.	Do you eat when you're not hungry?	____	____
2.	Do you go on eating binges for no apparent reason?	____	____
3.	Do you have feelings of guilt and remorse after overeating?	____	____
4.	Do you give too much time and thought to food?	____	____
5.	Do you look forward with pleasure and anticipation to the moments when you can eat alone?	____	____
6.	Do you plan these secret binges ahead of time?	____	____
7.	Do you eat sensibly before others and make up for it alone?	____	____
8.	Is your weight affecting the way you live your life?	____	____

21

9. Have you tried to diet for a week (or longer), only to fall short of your goal? ____ ____

10. Do you resent the advice of others who tell you to "use a little will power" to stop overeating? ____ ____

11. Despite evidence to the contrary, have you continued to assert that you can diet "on your own" whenever you wish? ____ ____

12. Do you crave to eat at a definite time, day or night, other than mealtime? ____ ____

13. Do you eat to escape from worries or trouble? ____ ____

14. Has your physician ever treated you for overweight? ____ ____

15. Does your food obsession make you or others unhappy? ____ ____

How did you score? If you answered yes to three or more of these questions, it is probable you have a compulsive-overeating problem or are well on the way to having one.[1]

I myself scored 100 per cent! I'm not certain in my own mind that three or four "yes" answers mean all that much. A certain proportion of normal thins in our society are compulsive *undereaters*. They are convinced they are fat when in fact they may be dangerously underweight. If you have been a normal-thin child, have maintained your normal weight within a small range during your adult years, and have recently put on a few pounds, have a little tummy roll, or have gone up a size or so, you are definitely *not* a compulsive overeater, no matter what you score on the test. You are a normal, slightly overweight adult who probably needs to go on a diet for a

[1] Reprinted by permission of Overeaters Anonymous, World Service Office, 2190 190th Street, Torrance, California 90504; (213) 320-7941.

short time and, perhaps, make a minor modification in your eating (or drinking) habits. Like many people, you probably get less exercise than previously and have unconsciously added a few calories here and there without noticing.

Unfortunately, a few girls in high school or college see themselves as grossly fat when they are quite thin. They diet themselves to the point of dangerous malnutrition. They may well be obsessive/compulsive people, but overeating is *not* their problem. (If you have ever worked in a clothing store, you are probably familiar with compulsive shoppers, people who buy and buy, returning several times a week. If you are a salesperson on commission you probably love them. Compulsive, yes. Overeaters, no.)

The profile of a compulsive overeater goes something like this. At about four, five, or six years of age, he or she became quite overweight compared to other children on the block. Efforts to make the child diet or reduce his or her intake met with tears of anger or frustration. The child was teased, called fat. At puberty the child made the first effort to lose weight, perhaps losing a substantial amount, only to regain what had been lost plus additional pounds. The typical cycle was as follows: three, four, or five years of substantial gain followed by a severely restricted diet and weight loss, a short period of pleasure and new clothes, then a return to binging and gross overeating, new weight gain, and usually the return to an even higher weight than before.

The compulsive overeater is usually bright; many can honestly be called intellectually brilliant. They tend to be bookworms and compulsive students—compulsive test takers —compulsive overachievers in an educational sense, perhaps compulsive overachievers in a career as well. In fact, many or most are compulsive in a variety of ways. One common compulsion is an obsession with perfection in anything he or she attempts. Since perfection is obviously impossible in our disorderly world, the result is abnormal frustration. And compulsive overeating.

We might run through some more questions. Have you ever stolen food? Hidden dirty dishes under your bed or in your bureau to conceal the fact from your parents? Did you lie about your out-of-the-house eating? Do you lie about it now?

How did you feel about athletics? About compulsory gym classes? Did you like yourself as a child, or as a teen-ager; do you like yourself now? (Be honest. Level with yourself.) Was either parent severely overweight? Was that parent a compulsive overeater, now that you think about it? Was food used as a substitute for love in your home? Did your parents put their arms around you much—hug you, kiss you? How did they reward you?

How do you really feel about sex? How did you feel about sex as a child? Do you really like to screw? (I mean *really* like to screw?) At what do you "draw the line" with members of the opposite sex? Why? How about sex with yourself? Do you still feel "funny" or guilty about masturbation? Why? Is it possible that "being fat" gets you out of sex situations you'd rather avoid? (Be honest. Being fat can be a first-class cover-up.) If you were truly thin, would you like sex more than you like it now? Would you like to get thin so you can screw better? (It's one of the best reasons for getting thin there is. If your thoughts are negative at this point, you might want to ask yourself some pointed questions. Maybe you'd really rather not be thin after all.)

Let's talk about eating. Do you conceive of a "good meal" in terms of taste or in terms of quantity? If you knew in advance that the small filet was better-tasting than the large T-bone, which would you order? How often do you order broiled chicken or fish in a restaurant when you are *not* on a diet? Can you eat *one* pretzel and leave the rest of the open bag alone? Can you do this by yourself when no one else is in the room? Does drinking turn you off food, or make you hungry? If you overdrink, do you also overeat? (Compulsive drinkers—alcoholics—tend not to eat when they drink. Many alcoholics who maintain their sobriety become compulsive overeaters.)

Have you ever bought a dozen doughnuts and eaten the entire dozen in one session? Have you ever done this and *forgotten* you had eaten them? Have you ever ordered food for three or four people in a take-out restaurant, gone home, and binged the entire amount? How do you do on candy? Can you eat one piece?

Do you panic if your refrigerator is low on food? (I went on a trip to the Colorado mountains once, by myself, and bought a case of army combat rations for the car . . . for an emergency! I used to steal army chocolate bars in Italy and gorge myself sick.) If you go to the supermarket for a quart of milk, what do you come home with? How do you feel about the Sara Lee counter? What foods do you prefer? What's your idea of a perfect meal? Would you order or eat the same meal in company with a group of thins—or is your ideal menu something better eaten alone?

By the way, how do you feel about buying clothes? Would you rather shop alone, or have your best friend or spouse come along with you?

One last set of questions, and strange ones, but questions I think are terribly important for reasons we shall discuss in a later chapter: *Does your best friend care how much you weigh? Does your wife, husband, or lover care how much you weigh? Is your best friend, spouse, or lover a normal thin?* If this individual is a normal thin and doesn't care whether or not you are overweight, I suspect you have a problem in your relationship and one you must face up to if you are ever to stop eating compulsively.

Many former compulsive overeaters find that losing weight is strangely threatening to former relationships they had assumed were rock-solid. Sometimes the loss of such a relationship (or the threat of such a loss) causes a return to compulsive overeating. In fact, many of my friends who have stopped eating compulsively have divorced *after* becoming normally thin. We will return to this problem later, but it is something to think about if you are reading this book to learn how to sincerely become thin and lose your compulsion to overeat.

Many or most compulsive overeaters are unable, for one reason or another, to take the first and most important step back to sanity: to identify oneself as a compulsive overeater and to admit this to others. If you are unable or unwilling to admit this one fact, that you are a compulsive overeater, then I cannot offer much hope. But if you flunked the short test at the beginning of this chapter, if you answered yes to many or most of the remaining questions, you are deluding yourself if you are unable to look yourself in the eye and say, "I am a compulsive overeater."

If you can, if you qualify, then this is your first assignment on the road back to sanity. *The very next person you meet, assuming this person is important in your life, I want you to say to him or her, "I just learned something important. I am a compulsive overeater."*

You will be pleasantly surprised how easy it is to say it and talk about it. Welcome back. You have taken the first step. Congratulations. The first step is the hardest. Having admitted your obsession is the beginning of sanity.

FIVE
ooooooooooo

> Any technique concerned with the other without the
> self, with behavior to the exclusion of experience, with
> the relationship to the neglect of the persons in relation,
> with the individuals to the exclusion of their relation-
> ship, and most of all, with an object-to-be-changed
> rather than a person-to-be-accepted, simply perpet-
> uates the disease it purports to cure.
> —R. D. Laing, *The Politics of Experience*

I say now what I think needs saying in a spirit of humility.
The medical profession with its devotion and its science has
saved my life on three occasions. It has not, however, cured my
obesity or my compulsive overeating. There are profound
reasons why this is so. My "lack of co-operation" and my
"lack of will power" are but the outer surface of reasons why
medicine has largely been unsuccessful, notoriously unsuccessful, in the treatment of the disease it calls obesity. Physicians
have not failed, however, for lack of trying. It is the philoso-

phy of medicine that fails the doctors, not the doctors who fail medicine.

A round ball rolling down an inclined plane is a *phenomenon*. The *cause*, postulated in elementary physics textbooks, is a product of gravity, friction, and the angle of decline of the plane. Given the force of gravity on earth, the friction of the surface, and the angle, the speed of the ball between any two given points can be calculated. If, however, the ball is a round man with a nagging wife and a hangover, a Republican voter with four children, a college graduate, a Catholic, and a resident of Houston, Texas, the formula becomes considerably more complicated. Traditional sociologists with a mathematical bent may claim the problem is not without rational solution, but even they resort to a somewhat weaseling statistical technique. They will talk about tendencies and not *that* man.

Bloody flux was the term used by early European physicians for the tendency of certain patients with dysentery to discharge bloody material. In other words, the bloody flux was a disease. Since certain potions concocted of eye of newt and lizard tail, along with bleeding by leeches and hot compresses, were found to do more apparent good than harm, they became prescriptions for the cure of the bloody flux. That is not to say the physicians knew the *cause* of the phenomenon they had named and prescribed for. Today one might suspect ulcers, cancer, or other reasons, but the vital symptoms remain unchanged from Henry VIII's time: bloody diarrhea. Any abnormal symptom, in medicine, is an indicant of an underlying cause: *disease*. All medicine consists of this: a patient with a symptom or symptoms; a suspected pathological condition; a series of tests designed to isolate the causative agent (the disease); and the administration of treatment powerful enough to cure the disease yet benign enough not to kill the patient.

(Probably all cancer is treatable. But most treatments would kill the patient.)

It seems to be a principle of medicine that *anything* that upsets the normal functioning of the patient's system is, by definition, a disease. So long as the physician deals in yellow fever, rabies, cancer, or the common cold (or other diseases of that ilk), the physician is on high ground. But when "disease" appears to be society- or personality-connected, the doctor has a problem. For example, hypertension (elevated blood pressure) is a "disease." (It is also a phenomenon, which is an additional problem.) Certain patients suffering from hypertension appear to fall into a statistical classification doctors have come to call Type A hypertension. These are patients who, among other things, tend to be overweight, are compulsive workers, have outgoing personalities, are self-motivated, and set high standards for themselves. What we have here is something like this: a grab bag of social/psychological traits plus several medical indicants, well mixed together, become something akin to anthrax: a disease. The patient suffers from Type A. Apparently what the doctor is now supposed to do is kick the Type A out of his patient . . . somehow or other. (One imagines his physician telling the President of the United States to resign and take employment as a mail clerk in the postal department.)

Sigmund Freud, a doctor of medicine from Austria, became the bridge across the stream from the bank of traditional disease so ably scienced by Pasteur, Koch, Lister, and the rest of the nineteenth-century medical scientists to a further, more murky, bank and a new set of diseases: neurosis, psychosis, paranoia, schizophrenia, and the rest.

But notice the difference. Malaria was a disease (a pathological condition) observable under a microscope and caused

29

by the injection of a living substance into the patient's blood stream by the bite of a particular variety of mosquito. If the malaria was difficult to immunize against, or to cure once one was infected, at least the mosquitoes could be DDT'd to death, or the swamps drained, or both.

But *paranoia is a set of symptoms*, roughly defined as a set of systemized delusions and the projection of personality conflicts that are ascribed to the personal hostility of others.[1] The definition changes slightly, depending on what book you read, and in no sense relates to any scientific agent of causality as simple as the force of gravity or as visible as the bacterium of anthrax. In these definitional terms, a Brooklyn mafioso with a contract on his head is probably damn paranoid. So is an infantry rifleman in combat. So were the Jews at Auschwitz. So was Nixon. In point of fact, if you, dear reader, were suddenly to be deprived of your civil rights and sent to a mental institution, you, too, would be paranoid beyond a shadow of medical doubt. Wouldn't you be convinced some enemy was out to get you? And the resident psychiatrist would listen to your complaints, probably shake his head, perhaps mutter, "Ach so!" and write "Paranoid" across your file.

If you are a compulsive overeater and grossly overweight in a society and culture that discriminate against fat people, I assure you that your delusions of persecution, your supposed paranoia, are real as real can be.

If you go to a conventional doctor of medicine you will be diagnosed as suffering from the *disease* of obesity. Your doctor will likely run a series of tests to find or eliminate such factors as glandular upset or other possible causatives. He will ask if your father or mother is obese. He will observe and test for other possible diseases, like hypertension or diabetes. About 98 per cent of the time he will diagnose your malady as "simple

[1] American College Dictionary (New York: Random House, 1960).

30

obesity," suggest the cause is overeating, prescribe a diet to reduce your weight, tell you to return periodically to be weighed, and sincerely shake your hand at the door.

(He might also prescribe dangerous drugs like Dexedrine. Then you will be an obese junkie.)

Your physician also will know, from sad experience, that your chances of losing weight *and maintaining the loss* are approximately zero! Unlike your trim, thin physician, *you have no will power*. He knows that. He also knows he has neither the time, the inclination, nor the training to probe deeper.

But what your doctor can do, and perhaps will do, is suggest you see his brother physician in the shaggy sport coat . . . a psychiatrist.

Your psychiatrist studied medicine at the same or a similar school as your physician, likewise earning an M.D. degree. Like the internist, he will take as his model for diagnosis and treatment the familiar disease/medical model, with this difference: his list of symptoms is largely inconclusive, almost impossible to verify by any scientific test, and seldom if ever acceptable to any two out of three of his professional peers. (If you dispute this, you may wish to read the medical testimony from the recent trial of *United States* v. *Patricia Hearst*.)

Because you are his fat patient in a thin society, you are probably paranoid, whatever that means precisely. Nobody really loves a fat man; and, apart from sexually screwed-up fatty chasers, the opposite sex generally finds fat women less than attractive. So, thinking you repulse members of society, you feel people do not appreciate the real "you" inside your body. Discriminated against by employers, potential lovers, dinner party hostesses, and the clothing industry to boot, you *are* paranoid.

You are also schizophrenic in the sense that your outer fat

shell and your inner self differ in character. Since you are two people (at least) in one, you withdraw frequently and cry, or closet yourself in a corner: schizophrenic manifestations, all.

(A girl once told a fat friend of mine she wanted to know "the real you." "For God's sake," he replied, "which one?")

Since you fail to conform to outside standards of beauty and eating habits, wear dowdy clothes because that's all fat people can find in the fat-people stores (half-size departments, Lane Bryant, "Big Man" store, and so forth), and fail to measure up to community employment standards ("attractive receptionist wanted by exciting advertising agency"), you obviously exhibit antisocial behavior.

And the more you talk to your psychiatrist about your lousy mother who substituted strawberry knishes for loving kisses, the more you confirm his diagnosis of you as a paranoid schizophrenic with a grave neurosis bordering on severe psychosis.

In place of livers, kidneys, and glands, Sigmund Freud substituted egos, ids, and superegos: areas that were considerably more difficult to X-ray. Instead of a slipped disc, you now had a displaced ego. Or you were orally fixated if you were fat. Four years ago the American Psychiatric Association removed homosexuality from its official list of "mental disorders." Yet recently Dr. Charles W. Socarides, clinical professor of psychiatry of the State University of New York's Downstate Medical Center, spoke as follows: ". . . it is scientific folly for psychiatry to normalize homosexual relations as if they had no psychopathology. . . . Homosexuality is not just an alternate life-style. *It is a devastating disease of psychological origin.*"[2]

This is no brief for (or against) homosexuality one way or another. But certainly what is no disease to one group and a

[2] *Newsweek* (October 25, 1976), p. 103. (Italics added.)

"devastating disease" to another is cold comfort to the layman on the couch. I take the position of the British psychologist R. D. Laing as sensible when he says: ". . . it seems to us that *without exception* the experience and behavior that gets labeled schizophrenic is a *special strategy that a person invents in order to live in an unlivable situation. . . .* The contradictions and confusions 'internalized' by the individual must be looked at in their larger social context."[3]

The point is that the medical model, whether that of the internist or the medically trained psychiatrist, with its emphasis on disease—cause—treatment—cure, is insufficient in many cases, and in the case of compulsive overeaters just plain doesn't work. If you doubt this, ask your doctor how many compulsively overeating patients of his have lost weight and successfully kept it off. And while you're about it, ask your psychiatrist the same question.

Incidentally, the latest medical explanation of obesity to come to my attention speculates that fat people have fat cells formed in childhood that retain a fat-gathering propensity throughout adult life. This may explain why some people gain weight faster than others. But it does not necessarily explain how the child got fat in the first place. Nor does it explain how my friend Marianne went from 340 pounds to 105 pounds and how she has remained at 105 pounds for four years *without dieting*.

What is disease? The fever and chills of malaria are the observed phenomena. Malaria is the disease. Hypertension (elevated blood pressure) is a phenomenon. Obesity (elevated weight) is a phenomenon. Then why are hypertension and obesity *diseases?* They are not. They are observed phenomena

[3] *The Politics of Experience* (New York: Pantheon Books, 1967), pp. 114–15. (Italics in original.)

indicating an underlying cause. In both cases, hypertension and obesity, the causes are at least partially psychological in origin and likely more social than psychological. In the case of obesity, I would contend, and bitterly, that compulsive overeating is the disease (if you want to call it that) and but one of many obsessive compulsions afflicting the human animal. Our concern should be with the social/psychological problems of the obese patient. If physicians are unable to treat compulsive overeating and accompanying obesity adequately, they should be prepared to direct the patient elsewhere.

As sociologists use the term, a *sanction* is a punishment visited on unruly members of a social group for breaking a social rule. Roughly speaking, "uncool" behavior is a social crime, calling for sanctions ranging from ostracism to just plain being frowned upon. For example, if you pick your nose in mixed company, you are liable to lose some friends; defending management in a tavern filled with union factory workers is liable to get you a cut lip.

Diets are special social sanctions imposed by social groups, significant others, or the self upon fat people for breaking a social rule: being fat. Let me be perfectly clear. *I do not believe a compulsive overeater should go on a diet.* You may wish to modify your diet, but that is not the same thing at all. (For all I know, your present diet may consist of nothing but chocolate-covered doughnuts. That must go. But you are *not* going on a "diet." This is not a "diet book.")

The trouble with weight-reducing diets is that they are designed by normal, healthy thins with degrees in nutrition *for people who are already normally thin.* I know compulsive overeaters who have lost over two hundred pounds. There is no way in hell they could lose two hundred pounds *and keep it off* (which they have) on any diet published in your Sunday newspaper supplement—or on the diet your physician hands out, either! In the last eighteen months I have lost about ninety pounds *on no diet at all.*

If you are a normal thin with eight or ten pounds to lose (that "little tummy bulge," as the magazines say), then any diet that restricts calories while providing at least some nutrition will work. It doesn't matter if the diet consists of grapefruit and meat loaf; is a drinking man's diet (I loved that one: lost two pounds on food and gained ten on iced gin); or is the Mayo, Johns Hopkins, Air Force, egg, or Linda Lovelace diet. You will lose your ten pounds. They all work. And they all take concentration, special shopping, special preparation, and will power, and are all designed to drive you and your family out of your collective skulls by the end of the second week.

Your typical "diet" states that by following the prescribed regime you will be "comfortably full with no appetite pains." It is to laugh. I never heard of a compulsive overeater who *ever* felt full. Bloated, yes. Ready to vomit, yes. Sweating and gagging, yes. But "full"—never! If I've got one more doughnut in the box or one more spoonful of ice cream in the carton, you know damn well where it's going to end up. I'm never "full."

They tell me that normal thins have a kind of little clock in their stomach that tells them when they're full—when it's time to quit eating. I know thins who can eat a raw carrot and a cracker and say they are "stuffed." It takes me a minimum of two roast ducks with dressing, several helpings of mashed potatoes and gravy, a quart of ice cream, and at least three pieces of chocolate fudge cake—and I still wouldn't be "full."

Compulsive overeaters on a "diet"—any diet—are constantly hungry. This hunger, dear thin, is real. It hurts. If it is psychosomatic, "in our heads," then it is a fiendishly clever illusion. And our hunger pains constantly serve to remind us that we are "on a diet"—ergo, different: fat people on a diet.

Our doctor, by his nods of approval or clucks of disapproval, reinforces our feelings of fatness when we get on his scale. He sets what seems an impossible goal. A 210-pound woman is told her "normal" weight is 115. (The last time she weighed 115 was in sixth grade, for heaven's sake.) We fats prep for a visit to the doctor as if we were participating in the Olympic Games. Take a laxative the night before—or an enema, perhaps. Get rid of fecal weight. Eat a slice of orange for breakfast, a bowl of consommé for lunch. Thirty minutes before weigh-in time: urinate. Push as hard as you can. Get rid of every last drop.

"That's fine, Mrs. Jones—197 today. Only 82 pounds to go. Do you feel all right?"

Feel all right? Shall we tell you thins what it feels like to be constipated for a year . . . for two years . . . to go four or five days between bowel movements?

"Yes, Doctor. I feel fine."

And the scales. Those damn scales. Mine at home weighs three pounds lighter than my doctor's scale. I think he rigs his that way to frustrate me. He weighs me fully dressed in stocking feet. I wear my lightest pair of pants, my lightest shirt, my narrow fabric belt instead of the heavy leather one with the brass buckle I normally have on. Down in the car, before my appointment, I shed my gold ring, my loose change, and my Zippo lighter.

Have you ever gotten up to urinate at 4:00 A.M., then stripped and weighed yourself at that ungodly hour to see if a pound had somehow flushed down the drain?

Like Gaul, all diets are roughly divisible in thee parts. In our first group we find those designed to reduce the caloric intake of the dieter. A calorie is a measurement of the energy value of food. It has been estimated that a moderately active person requires 12 to 15 calories daily for each pound of body weight. Thus a 150-pound person burns around 2,250 calories a day. This depends, however, on your individual body metabolism, the amount of energy you expend, and the "efficiency" of your particular body machinery. It is true that some people lose weight on 2,250 calories and others gain. But this is not a valid excuse for weighing 275 pounds.

Calorie-deficient diets all work on the same principle. They provide you with less food than you need, thereby causing the body to make up the deficit by burning excess body fat as fuel.

The more you weigh, the more calories you need to sustain your weight. This is very important. It is the reason why a compulsive overeater with a severe obesity problem can lose weight without "dieting." If you need 4,000 calories to sustain 275 pounds and your doctor reduces your caloric intake to 900 calories, you will obviously lose weight for the length of time you can stand a 900-calorie-per-day diet.

But if you consume 2,250 calories a day, you will also lose weight. In fact, if your metabolism is normal and your energy output is normal, you will lose weight until you weigh 150 pounds! It is just that simple.

All you have to do is eat like a normal human being who

weighs what you want to weigh. That is the secret. No more, no less. No magic. In fact, no diet. What I am going to do is turn you into a normal, sane human being. (If that's what you want to be.)

The second group of weight-reduction systems is based on interfering, chemically or otherwise, with the normal functioning of your body. This is bad country. This is the valley of the dolls. If you take certain drugs, primarily from the amphetamine group that includes Dexedrine, your metabolism will become so screwed up that you will lose weight—just like any other normal speed freak. As one woman on Dexedrine told me, "It was wonderful. I got all my housework done between 2 and 4 A.M."

This second weight-reduction system is the secret of the "diet factory" you see advertised in your newspaper or over television. "Lose 40 or 50 pounds the first month without dieting!" For $40 or $50 a week, they hand you a bottle of pills (perhaps $7 worth of pills if purchased on prescription from your druggist). You take the pills. You lose weight. And after a few weeks, if you aren't getting the same "kick" as in the beginning, they will give you more pills, for more money. One college girl I know was spending $150 a week on her pills. In three months this girl lost about 55 pounds. In the fourth month she tried to slit her wrists. Luckily her roommate found her bleeding in the bathtub and called the paramedics. She lived, but the clinic is still open, still advertising, and still turning lovely young girls with compulsive overeating problems into speed freaks.

Another group on our second list is the "clinics" giving injections of strange substances like urine from pregnant women. (If you are a normal thin, just imagine the sheer desperation of anyone who would take such treatment with the dream of being thin like you.)

Still other methods involve water loss: wrapping you in special sheets to increase perspiration, pills to increase urination, and so on.

"Quick weight loss" clinics in our second group flourish for two reasons: first, because obese compulsive overeaters are so desperate they will do anything to lose weight; and second, because reputable members of the medical profession allow less-than-honest, greedy colleagues to continue to practice. The police are powerless if the clinic operates under the ownership and supervision of a member of the medical profession. And even more unfortunately, some physicians specializing in "obesity" continue to push pills from the façade of a respectable office. They practice a cruel fraud on innocent, gullible people who come to them with anguished souls, praying they have found salvation. At best they find a hoax . . . at worst, death.

The third diet group is a combination of the first two. A "quick weight loss" clinic offers urine shots, for example, but puts its patients on a 600-calorie diet "just to make sure." Or a physician puts his patient on a 900-calorie diet, then prescribes amphetamines to be certain he or she loses weight.

Certain diets are both low-caloric and system-screwing-up at the same time. One such is the Dr. Atkins Diet.[1] Atkins' diet is basically high-protein, high-fat, and zero-carbohydrate. The purpose of this diet is to force you into ketosis: a serious chemical upset of the system that causes the body to fight back by burning fat. Prolonged ketosis can lead to kidney and

[1] Robert C. Atkins, *Dr. Atkins' Diet Revolution* (New York: David McKay Co., 1972).

liver damage and a build-up of uric acid that may precipitate diseases such as gout.[2] Others of this ilk include the Stillman Quick Weight Loss Diet, the Air Force Diet (disclaimed by the Air Force), the Mayo Clinic Diet (not recognized by the Mayo Clinic), and the Boston Police Diet (not recognized by the Boston Police Department, the Air Force, *or* the Mayo Clinic).[3]

Any diet that eliminates protein, fat, or carbohydrates, either entirely or drastically, is liable to be life-threatening if used for prolonged periods to treat severe obesity. If you want to lose ten or twelve pounds, it's maybe okay—but not for weight losses in excess of twenty-five pounds.

A second system for weight loss that has been helpful for some compulsive overeaters is the Weight Watchers clubs. They do work. They also work better for some people than for others. To my mind they have two major drawbacks: first, they are organized to turn a profit for the stockholders and the franchise owner; second: they tend to be authoritarian in flavor. If you like to trade recipes for low-calorie chocolate fudge brownies, such clubs are your place. They do not really discourage your compulsive overeating. Rather, they let you continue to eat compulsively but on lower-calorie goodies. Diet clubs of this kind are costly, they push a brand of products, and they encourage crash dieting by setting up competition between members to see who can lose the most weight.

"Would you believe that one of our new members, Sylvia Jones, has lost seventeen pounds in one month! Come on, folks, let's hear it for Sylvia. Give the thin little lady a big hand!"

[2] Cf. Nikki and David Goldbeck, *The Dieter's Companion* (New York: McGraw-Hill, 1975), pp. 25–28.
[3] Goldbeck, op. cit., pp. 20–28.

(That noise you hear is Sylvia crashing to the floor the following Tuesday.)

Commercial diet clubs depend on a dynamic leader, one with hair like Jack Kennedy and a forceful approach. Marine Corps drill instructors probably do nicely. (Mine was just loaded with cute psychological bags of tricks, like hauling in a thirty-pound box of lard to show us what Sylvia lost.) He praises the big losers and shames the gainers. He puts on a terrific show. But what he doesn't do is eliminate compulsive overeating. (If he did, maybe he'd go out of business.) By switching you from high-calorie to low-calorie chocolate cake and encouraging you to eat five or six meals a day, however low-calorie, he is not teaching his members to be normal thins. His club is trying to turn you into a compulsive overeater of low-calorie food. That's not the answer.

Another system of weight reduction presently in vogue utilizes the pop psychology of behaviorism: reward/punishment therapy. Basically, this is how you train a dog. If it messes the floor, you beat it. If it defecates outside on your neighbor's lawn, you pat its furry little head. I do not like behavioral training. I do not like people sticking pins in me or giving me electric shocks, no matter what good purpose may be involved. If behavioral training really works on people the way it does on rats, we can look forward to 1984 when some Hitler type will begin training the citizenry. Enough.

You have several other options not previously covered. You can have your jaws wired shut, you can have a hunk removed from your intestine, you can fast, and, finally, you can eat all you want of a new kind of goo developed by medical science that has absolutely no food value at all. But you can compulsively eat all the goo you want. (On October 29, a group of doctors presented the goo scheme to the NBC television

"Today" show. When the doctors were asked if the patient would resume compulsive overeating after the goo fast ended, the doctors said they were working on that.)

Let us repeat the two most important steps presented thus far:

1. *Admit to yourself and to those nearest and dearest to you that you are a compulsive overeater.*

2. *Understand that you do not need a deprivation diet to lose weight. If you eat the same diet as normal thins, and exercise as much as they, you will eventually be a normal thin yourself.*

The sperm of the male and the egg of the female are quite different from the other cells of the body. Within each is a single strand of a complex protein nucleic-acid substance biologists call DNA. Each strand carries, in biologic code, the entire set of instructions necessary to create life: the pattern for your fingernails, heart, liver, hair; instructions on when and how cells should begin growing and when they should stop growing; the complete blueprints and specifications for a body and career from conception to old age and death. When sexual intercourse takes place and one sperm (of millions) enters the egg in the female oviduct, the male and female DNA strands unite, twirl together, and wind themselves into a double helix. By doing so they combine the characteristics of the male and the female into a new being—part him and part her. No two children of the same parentage will be quite alike, each will differ importantly, yet each child will contain part of the characteristics of each parent.

Conventional psychology speaks of the unique personality of the child, just as religion regards every newborn child as possessing an almighty soul. Yet neither may be entirely correct.

If a child is born in a forest, deserted by its parents like the mythical Tarzan of the Apes, and raised by the animal creatures of that forest, it will not be, it will never be, a human being, no matter what its DNA pattern. Nor will that child have a human personality, nor, I submit, will it have a soul. It will be an animal.

A new human being begins to develop what we call individual personality at the instant it is born and is acted upon by—and reacts toward—other human beings. The fetus at full term is like a magnificent computer, dwarfing anything the likes of IBM ever conjectured. But like any new computer, its tapes are blank. It may instinctively suck food from a nipple, cry, blink its eyes, or move its limbs, but education—the awareness of human life *and its own life*—is just beginning.

I want you to imagine for a minute, if you will, that you are a runner in a long-distance race. (That you *can* imagine such a thing is part of the wonder of what I have to say.) As you run along, you will find yourself conducting a dialogue between two people: let us call them *I* and *Me*. The *I* protests. The race is too long, the *I* is tired, his legs are beginning to cramp, his chest burns from lack of oxygen. But *Me* urges *I* along. "Stick it out," *Me* says. "You must keep going. Catch up on the man in front of you. Forget the pain. You can do it. Keep driving . . . faster."

A University of Chicago professor named George Herbert Mead first called attention to this phenomenon in the 1930s.[1]

[1] *Mind, Self and Society* (Chicago, Ill.: University of Chicago Press, 1934).

What Mead said was this: *We learn to deal with society by taking the part of other members of society.* (Mead called this "the generalized other.") If you want to play baseball, Mead said, you literally have to be able to play every position on the team *in your head.* If you are shortstop and a ball is hit to you while a runner is on first base, you must know you touch second and throw to the first baseman for a doubleplay. You must know *where* to throw to the first baseman because you must, for a split instant, *be* the first baseman.

You cannot play checkers or chess unless you take the part of your opponent. If you go to a cocktail party, you can chat with other people intelligently only if you know what they expect you to say. You can do this because you rehearse your role. For an instant, *you play the part of the other.*

We learn to do this, Mead said, when we are children. As a child we can be lion hunter, deep-sea diver, mother, father, whatever we want to be. And children's games such as hide-and-seek are really practice times for learning to become socialized human beings. Where do you hide? You hide where you think the others can't find you, of course. And how do you find such a place? You find it by being, for a moment, the other children. The more you play the game, the more skillful you become. Your success at hiding is dependent on your ability to play the part of the others. You become a successful actor on the social stage.

The child also learns to deal with approval and disapproval, which are indicants of how well or how poorly he or she plays the game. Children are blunt, honest, and cruel to a degree almost unknown in the adult world. The most popular child among children is the one who elicits the most approval —and the least disapproval—from peers. The variety and multiplicity are endless. We learn successful sex roles: how to be a

46

"boy" and how to be a "girl." We also begin to learn a differentiated role: to be "accepted," yet different. We develop an individual ego personality of our own. One child learns to play the leader of the group; another, perhaps, to be the wise counselor. Another learns that a comic role is acceptable.

And some of us learn to be fat.

What I am suggesting is something like this: we learn to play a certain role in childhood by internalizing the expectations of the other children and adopting these expectations into our own "style" of action. Thus our own unique personality is forged: a product of our genetic inheritance *plus* our peculiar method of handling the reactions of significant others. These most basic fundamentals of our personality, our collective "Me," enter the computer tapes in our head when the tapes are mostly blank and uncluttered by the multitudinous junk we have soaked up and forgotten. (I'll bet you can remember more about the kids you played with in the early days of elementary school than most of the people you've met since.)

When I was five years old, I became critically ill and spent over three months in the hospital. The following year I missed first grade because my parents and the doctor felt I was not strong enough to play with other children and attend school. I spent most of that year in California with my grandparents, being tutored in first grade subjects and cut off from children my age. A great effort was made to "build me up." It succeeded. By second grade I was a fat kid. And I was different from other second grade boys in two ways. First, I had missed an entire year of peer group activity. (I quite simply didn't know how to act and react in the blunt, honest, and cruel world of second grade boys.) And second, I was a fat, unathletic kid. My peers treated me the way kids treat a fat kid. And I responded. *I learned to play the fat-kid role.*

My father was a compulsive overeater and I was his eldest child. I suspect, from some things he told me once in an uncharacteristic moment of self-confession, that he, too, had been a fat, picked-on kid who had also learned to play *his* role as a fat man in thin society. I remember one of the few times he ever admonished me about overeating: "George . . . I just don't want you to have the troubles I had as a kid." My younger brothers and my sister, like my mother, are normal thins. This is perfectly natural because they already had one fat member of the sibling group—me. The role was already taken. I, of course, was their bad example.

I strongly suspect, although I cannot prove it, that what I have said so far in this chapter explains why my many previous attempts to lose weight were so futile and why even now I have so much difficulty thinking thin. I have gone through my life (somewhat unhappily I must confess) playing the role of the fat man in thin society—the role I anticipated people wanted me to play—and even if I lost enough weight to be considered "thin," I wasn't comfortable in a thin role. Even though I have a thin body, I continue to have a "fat" head.

Nor do the relatives and friends I know from my fat days consider me thin. What they say to me goes something like this: "Oh . . . you've lost a lot of weight, haven't you. You look *good*." (Whatever that means.) *"You must feel a lot better now."*

What they mean is that they are slightly ill at ease around me because they aren't quite certain how I will act around them, now that I am thin. I am a new person, not their old fat friend. And frankly, I don't know how they expect me to act, either.

As a compulsive overeater, you are an antisocial animal in a world of rule-following social behavior. In the language of sociology, you are a deviant. One sociologist, Howard S. Becker, has formulated a unique approach to the study of deviance.[2] A deviant, Becker says, is a special kind of person who cannot be trusted to live by the rules accepted by the group. But the person thus *labeled* an outsider may not accept the rules by which he or she is being judged and may not regard those who judge as competent or legitimately entitled to do so. Hence the rule-breaker may feel his or her judges are "outsiders."

According to Becker, the medical profession has accepted the lay judgment of something (obesity and compulsive overeating in our case) as deviant or undesirable. The physician, applying his medical model of phenomenon—cause—cure, labels obesity a "disease" and communicates this label to the patient. This is central to Becker's thesis: *Social groups create deviance by making the rules whose infraction constitutes deviance; deviant behavior is behavior that people so label; and deviance is the product of a process that involves responses of other people to the behavior.*

Becker says the first step in building what he calls a "career of deviance" is the experience of being caught and publicly labeled a deviant (being called "fat" by significant others, in our case). He (or she) may label *himself* a deviant because of what he has done and punish himself in one way or another for his behavior. Indeed, the deviant may *want* to be caught and perpetrates his deviant act in such a way that he is almost sure he will be. Treating a person as a deviant is a self-fulfilling prophecy. To be labeled "fat" in a thin world, by others and the self, is treatment designed to ensure fatness just

[2] Howard S. Becker, *Outsiders* (Glencoe, Ill.: Free Press, 1963).

as surely as labeling a boy "fairy" might guarantee a homosexual career.

But while being labeled "fat" has certain social consequences, it also has rewards. It produces anxiety in certain instances, yet reduces anxiety in others. Being fat can be an excellent cop-out.

A normal-thin child is expected to play certain social roles in the peer group. Depending somewhat on sex, you are supposed to be reasonably competent at tree climbing, ball throwing, running and hiding games, and, later, at baseball, football, and the like. Some years ago the seaside California town in which I live was in the midst of a surfing craze. Boys were naturally expected to master the difficult technique of surfing: a sport requiring a high degree of balance and co-ordination. Girls in turn were expected to be thin and tanned, and to have sun-streaked hair, attractive figures, and surfer boy friends. Fathers and mothers expected their sons and daughters to participate. I know more than one fat kid whose father bought him a surfboard in the quite unreasonable expectation that the poor kid would become a surfing star. If the boy did not have the requisite athletic ability to surf, if the girl lacked physical beauty, they were "out of it"—*outsiders*. Being fat meant being an outsider, but it was also an excuse. The expectations of others weren't as high. In one sense the anxiety level of the compulsively overeating teen-ager was raised, yet in another fashion it was reduced. Being fat was a cop-out for not being a surfing star. Similarly, a boy whose father expects him to star in Little League baseball or a girl whose mother expects her to excel in high school dating games may use compulsive overeating to eliminate the problem and thus reduce anxiety produced by peer and parental pressure. (You may remember the old "Our Gang" comedy films. The gang had one fat member, played, as I recollect, by Spanky McFarland. He had a definite role: the fat clown.)

Laud Humphreys is the author of an interesting book entitled *Tearoom Trade*, a study of male deviants who inhabit public washrooms for the purpose of engaging in illicit sex.[3] Humphreys found, surprisingly, that 54 per cent of the public restroom deviants he studied were married and living with wives. They were ". . . lonely and isolated, lacking success in either marriage bed or work, unable to discuss their three best friends because they didn't have any."[4] These "tearoom" encounters, according to Humphreys, are deliberate high-risk games. Getting caught is the penalty. Sexual thrill is the pay-off. Getting caught, however, is absolution for the deviant's secret sins. If he wins, he hates himself afterward. It is, like compulsive overeating, a no-win game.

As Samuel B. Hadden said in a 1967 *Harper's* article:[5] "As social control agents impress upon members of a deviant group that they are 'sick,' so they will become." What this chapter has been all about is this: as fat children are labeled "fat" by parents, peers, and significant others (such as the family doctor), so they will become. Once structured into a social role and labeled "fat," we tend to continue playing this role for the rest of our days. If the former fat becomes thin, he or she experiences difficulty in adjusting to the role of "thin." The result is frustration. The goal of losing weight and becoming a normal thin brings new problems, role changes, and role reversals that the child (or adult) is unable to cope with. The new image is not rewarding in ultimate reality. The result is frus-

[3] Laud Humphreys, *Tearoom Trade* (Chicago, Ill.: Aldine Publishing Company, 1970).
[4] Humphreys, op. cit., p. 117.
[5] Samuel B. Hadden, "A Way Out for Homosexuals," *Harper's* (March 1967).

tration and a return to compulsive overeating, a kind of "damn you, I'll show you, I'll get fat again" syndrome. And it has not escaped my notice that this hypothesis has significant implications for society's failure to "reform" almost all deviant behavior, including alcoholism, sexual deviance, and criminal deviance.

But as we shall see, there is hope.

EIGHT

ooooooooooooooo

Each to each a looking-glass
Reflects the other that doth pass.

As we see our face, figure, and dress in the glass, and
are interested in them because they are ours, and pleased
or otherwise with them according as they do or do not
answer to what we should like them to be; so in imag-
ination we perceive in another's mind some thought
of our appearance, manners, aims, deeds, character,
friends, and so on, and are variously affected by it.
                    —Charles W. Cooley, *Social Organization*

Our previous chapter was concerned with an interesting hypothesis. Let us restate it once more:

*You cannot learn to be thin in a group of thins. You will al-
ways be allotted your old, fat role. You will always remain a
fat man or woman who is on a diet.*

My mother and father—like most mothers and fathers, I
guess—always remember me as I *was*. My adult accom-

plishments, whatever they might be, seem to puzzle them. My character and personality as a child are, to them, my character and personality now. My brothers and sister recall more of my childhood foibles than of my adult doings. My forty-eight-year-old younger brother tends to remind me on frequent occasions of the time I bashed him over the head with a ball bat (an incident that seems to have made a considerable impression on his head). My sister remembers how I teased her unmercifully when we were children. Whatever I say to her now, she has that petulant look in her eye, wondering if she is being cruelly teased once again. If ever I attend a high school reunion for the class of '41, no matter how thin and trim I appear now, I shall always be "fat George" to my classmates. You aren't going to shed your compulsive-overeater image or your fat role in the company of your family or your old thin friends.

Then *what*, you ask, and *how?* Okay. Here is the second part of our working hypothesis:

You can learn to be thin only in a group of fats and, by becoming thin, let them assign you the thin role.

A friend of mine, Professor James P. Driscoll of Sonoma State University in California, spent upwards of a year living in a San Francisco skid row hotel inhabited by transsexual prostitutes. A transsexual is a male who is convinced, for one reason or other, that he is really a girl in a male body (or a female who believes she is a man in a woman's body). The ultimate goal of the male transsexual is to "pass": to literally become a girl—mentally, sociologically, and physically—by taking female hormones and having his penis and testicles surgically removed and a vagina built in their place. Professor Driscoll is convinced that male transsexuals began to think of themselves as female during their early childhood, that this led

54

to their taking the passive (or female) role in high school homosexual encounters, and that they finally enter the transsexual subculture because it is the only society in which they can exist, no matter how uncomfortably. Since the skid row transsexual's social deviance is so extreme, so revolting, to heterosexual society, he is forced underground and into a highly secret, deviant subculture.

The skid row transsexual seeks the only source of employment open to him. Posing as a woman, he "hooks" as a street prostitute in the Tenderloin, serving his male client orally or anally. As you can imagine, it is a rough trade. Savage beatings from indignant clients are routine parts of "her" existence.

The hotel in which Driscoll and his wife lived was a literal "training school for women" complete with daily courses in make-up, hair style, the proper wearing of feminine clothing, eye movements, flirting behavior, hip movements—all the little signs that sexually distinguish male from female in ordinary society. The "girls" all took huge doses of female hormones, thus growing "breasts" and redistributing body fat. Facial and body hair were removed. The ultimate product was a "girl," complete in every detail save two: sex organs and, if you observed closely, an Adam's apple.

(Driscoll and his wife were accepted for a number of reasons: primarily because Mrs. Driscoll acted as drama coach for the "girls"; because Professor Driscoll kept them supplied with Bourbon; and because the Driscolls were kind, considerate, and loving toward their "girls"—an attitude transsexuals seldom receive from outside straights. I have been introduced to several of the Driscolls' "girls." Believe me, you would never know!)

There is no possible way a transsexual could ever learn to "pass" in the company of his family, siblings, or old friends.

Friends and family disowned them; having allotted them the "fairy" role in high school, they could view any change to femininity only as for the worse, not the better.

Every small-group subculture develops leader-follower patterns of informal social organization, and the transsexuals in the hotel were no different. According to Driscoll, the "girl" who passed the most successfully, acted the sexual role of female with the greatest degree of proficiency, was the social star. The most mannish, the stupid, the clumsy, or the hairy were the deviants. (As you can see, the definition of *deviant* is in the eye of the beholder.) In order to become "girls," these male transsexuals cut themselves off from the world of male straights and gathered together in a subculture of transsexuals. Their ultimate goal, however, was to take the next step: *to enter the female world with confidence and complete acceptance.*[1]

Your problem, if you are a compulsive overeater who also happens to be fat, is not entirely different from that of the "girls" mentioned above. Losing weight and becoming physically thin is only part of your problem, just as growing breasts and removing body hair was only part of the "girls'" problem. Like them, you must *learn* to be someone you have never been before: a thin human being. This is the trouble with the standard medical cure for obesity (among others). Doctors can cure your physical obesity; if all else fails, they can wire your

[1] The above is taken from the unpublished M.A. thesis of James P. Driscoll, San Francisco State University, San Francisco, California, plus private conversations with Professor Driscoll. It might be mentioned that Driscoll was instrumental in gaining police support for the "girls" and ending former harassment, much of which centered around arrests for using women's washrooms in San Francisco public buildings. A "woman" would be arrested for using *either* the men's or women's rest room. The girls were in a no-win situation with the police.

jaws or cut out a hunk of your intestine. They can hospitalize you and fast you thin. *But they cannot make you feel thin* because that is a social/psychological problem and not a medical problem at all. Even a thin psychologist or a normal-thin encounter group will fail because you will continue to play the role you were conditioned to play since childhood: the fat member of the group.

Your problem, like that of Driscoll's "girls," is one of learning to "pass" in the thin world as a normal thin. When you do that, you graduate. You may still be a compulsive overeater but, I submit, you will not compulsively overeat.

If you are a compulsive overeater, as I am, I would like to ask you a personal question. When was the last time you had a gut-level, down-to-earth conversation about being fat with a man or woman who is fat like yourself?

If you answered "Never," you are in the same league as I. I had never in my entire life, until last year, talked to a fellow compulsive overeater about being fat. And when I did, it was the greatest miracle in the world for us both. We had assumed all our lives that we were utterly unique: The only human beings in the world with heads full of fat-people troubles and problems. It was a strange conversation. We both fenced around for a while, giving one another that same old bull about "really not eating much" and "gaining weight just by looking at food" and "malfunctioning glands" and "water retention" and all the complete crap we fats have been feeding thins and ourselves for years. Finally I took the first step.

"I'm a compulsive overeater. *That's MY real problem.* How about you?"

That opened the dam. That man proceeded to pour his soul out on the floor—as I did mine. We found, to our surprise and bewilderment, that our childhood experiences were about the same, that we had each made repeated vows to "go on a diet," had lost huge amounts of weight, had regained the weight and more besides, that we loved to eat alone, to glut alone, and even that our experiences with doctors had been about the same. That man and I remain fast friends although he continues to eat compulsively and is not yet ready to take a further step toward sanity. The point is we both learned a fundamental fact: compulsive overeaters share common problems and common feelings. We *do* have a base for sharing.

Safe-crackers, bank robbers, transsexuals, and prostitutes live in subcultures of their own kind. Drug addicts, unless they are secret dopers, share a common culture and language: the argot of drugs. As the movie *The Sting* vividly illustrated, con men have a society all their own. But alcoholics and compulsive overeaters are *secret* deviants, living in the hell of their own mind. Alcoholics sit side by side in bars, drinking and talking together for years about everything under the sun except the one thing that really matters that they share in common: their addiction to alcohol. But even the alcoholic, until he reaches the final stages of addiction, manages to function, albeit painfully, in the normal world. Your star salesman who does such a good job of entertaining customers may be an alcoholic but keeps himself under reasonable control, and you're never going to know until the time comes when his self-control fails.

But the compulsive overeater carries his stigmata under his size 52 suit for all the world to see. The girl in the 54DD bra carries her advertisement with her. So does the young girl in the "Chubbie" dress her mother brought home to her crying child.

(When I was in seventh grade my father decided I needed a suit to wear to my grandparents' fiftieth wedding anniversary party. I still have a photograph of me in that suit at that party. It was tailor-made, by a cheap tailor, a horrible tentlike hairy thing made out of some kind of smelly tweed. God, how I remember that suit!)

Perhaps because fat people are so visible, perhaps because they feel so terrible about being fat, they tend to avoid each other's company. Certainly each has such deep inward hurt he or she would not dream of adding to the grief of another compulsive overeater.

The Menninger Foundation of Topeka, Kansas, conducts educational programs on human behavior for businessmen and other professionals. Dr. Roy Menninger, president of the foundation, said recently that the setting of the seminars makes it possible to ask business leaders whether they have someone to talk to. "The answer," said Roy Menninger, "is appalling. The majority do not have anyone. They have become sold on the idea that being competent and effective at work means repressing feelings and this belief spreads to their personal environment at home.

"Many executives depreciate themselves as objects of worth," continued Dr. Menninger. "They feel it is what they do, not what they feel that makes them real, and that if they couldn't do those things no one would look up to them. . . . Executives who become aware of their problem ask themselves what has happened to cause them to suppress their capacity to have feelings. We ought to have a concept of mental health maintenance so that each person must engage in this kind of dialogue and structure his or her life so he doesn't have to hire a psychiatrist as a paid friend."[2]

If top business executives are unable to express their feelings to their family or associates, small wonder that fat compulsive overeaters who have been social victims since childhood find it difficult to communicate with one another. This is part of the

[2] Harry Nelson in the Los Angeles *Times* (October 27, 1976), pp. C-1, 2.

reason they drag themselves to physicians' offices, to psychiatrists, to weight clinics and pill pushers. They are screaming for help and they aren't getting any. What they're getting is being told they have no will power, that they're fat and sloppy, that they're sick people. Well, hell—they already know *that!* They've tried talking to the doctors. They tried talking to their parents. Some of them tried talking to their thin friends or thin wives or husbands. It's time compulsive overeaters tried talking to one another. That's where the love and compassion really is, folks. Right in one another's arms.

If you are fat and you have a circle of fat compulsively overeating friends you can really relate to on a one-to-one gut level, something pretty wonderful is going to start happening. If I have found out anything at all about fat people, I haven't found it out talking to myself. I haven't found much in any of the books I've read (written by thin doctors and thin nutritionists) that I didn't know already. What I have learned about myself I have learned from my wonderful friends who are compulsive overeaters.

I learned how we shared almost identical childhood experiences, how much we all hated clothes from the Chubbies or Husky department, how we felt about being the last one chosen for a game of tag or sand-lot baseball, how we felt the night of the high school prom, how we felt in our tent suit or tent dress at our thin brother or sister's wedding . . . how the personnel manager looked when he told us he had several more people to see before he made his decision. We learned the dark night in our soul was the same blackness in each one of us. We learned to cry together because we found a tear from one was a tear from us all. And finally, we began to laugh a little, too. With each other and, at last, at each other. And that was the best of all.

Slowly but surely, under our new program and with love for each other, we began to lose weight. The longer we had been in the program, the more we lost. (Not all of us lost weight. We continued to pour nothing but love on each other no matter what our weight. We were friends, not contestants.) But those of us who did lose substantial amounts of weight and began to appear at meetings in our new, thin clothing began to notice that a new thing was happening. In the eyes of our friends, *we were thins*. Thins among fats. They still regarded us as loving friends: we could see that in their eyes. But they began to look up to us as successful examples of what the program could do for each one.

Among our fat compulsively overeating friends, we became normal thins. And as we began slowly to think of ourselves as normal thins, that's just what we finally became. Normal thins with fat friends.

What is this program and how does it work? How do you find a loving circle of fat friends? That's what I'm going to explain. What I became and how it works.

Let us briefly review the important steps so far:

1. *Admit to yourself and to those nearest and dearest to you that you are a compulsive overeater.*

2. *Understand that you do not need a deprivation diet to lose weight. If you eat the same diet as normal thins, and exercise as much as they, you will eventually be a normal thin yourself.*

3. *You learn to be thin only in a group of fats and, by becoming thin, let them assign you the thin role.*

NINE

ooooooooooo

Moslems refer to Jews and Christians as "people of the book." By this book they mean the Bible. The Bible sets us of the Western world apart from all other people by giving us something quite unique: a vivid sense of time and history. We are corrupted by time and passionately devoted to our own history. A newborn child inherits, along with biology, the history of his or her ancestors and parents' expectations for the future. His or her life is structured with "that which was done wrong yesterday" and "that which must be accomplished tomorrow." The insurance annuity purchased for the child's future college education is a vast monument to parental expectations. The F on the arithmetic test is a substantial blot on the child's record. All our life has become a sadness for the folly of the past and resolves to do better in the future. Our life is a stream in time dotted with little islands of good and bad deeds, remembrances of things past. Our tomorrows are the fearful rapids that lie ahead.

When I step on my scale to weigh myself and find the indicator is up a pound or two, I am filled with guilt and sorrow for the folly of yesterday. My resolve to lose ten more pounds in the coming month is a savage dictation. But this is nonsense! What is done is done. And I surely cannot lose ten pounds *today*.

Yesterday is gone forever, beyond any hope of recall. Tomorrow may never come. But surely I can do what needs doing *today*.

I vividly recall my visits to the doctor. The recording of the weight I had gained on his scale, the fresh penning of it in his notebook, were all too legible accompaniments to his stern lectures on my past indulgences, graphic monuments to my compulsive overeating. I stood before him like an accused prisoner in the dock, awash with guilt, self-pity, anger, and frustration.

"But don't tell me what a fool I was yesterday," I screamed silently. "Don't you understand? I'm here *today!* That's why I came to you. I'm here *today!*"

Then my doctor handed me a printed set of instructions with lists of foods I was to eat and lists of foods I was not to eat, with rations like "Beef: 4 oz." and "Shrimp: 4 small," and admonitions like "All meat should be broiled, not fried" or "Artificial sweeteners only."

"If you follow this diet," he said more or less brightly, "you should lose 10 or 12 pounds a month. Your normal weight should be about 175 pounds. All it takes is a little co-operation and will power. Just consider this your goal. I'm sure you won't have any trouble if you'll just follow these instructions. And by the way, be sure to drop in every two weeks so my nurse can weigh you. Good luck!"

Good luck. Lots of luck. Patently I had been a bad boy in the *past*. I was expected to be a good boy in the *future*. By

63

just showing a little will power I would be "normal" in the future. Not one word about *today*.

Well, I don't live that way any more. I don't give a good continental damn about yesterday. Yesterday is gone, I cannot bring it back, I cannot undo what is done. I cannot beat my head with the stupidity of my past.

Nor do I know what tomorrow will bring; nor do I care. It might be good. It might be bad. I don't know. Tomorrow I might be rich, powerful, a hero or a bank president. On the other hand, I might have cancer, be run over by a car, or fall down a flight of stairs, in which case I don't want to know about it. I'm done with being paranoid about the past or compulsive about tomorrow. I live my life *today* . . . one day at a time . . . for the rest of my life.

I know this violates every precept of Western society and civilization. I know this and I don't care. For me each day is quite sufficient in itself.

I have a lot of things to get done *today*. I have this chapter to write. I need to deposit money in my checking account. The lawn needs mowing. My wife and I are going out to a restaurant tonight and I must phone for a reservation. The dog needs fresh water in his dish. And I must consider what I will have for lunch and what I will order for dinner in the restaurant.

What I will *not* do today is eat compulsively. I had a normal, nourishing breakfast this morning. For lunch I plan to have a bacon, lettuce, and tomato sandwich on whole wheat toast, with a glass of milk. I think I will order a small steak, salad, and cottage cheese at the restaurant. Perhaps, if I feel in the mood, I will have a glass of white wine before dinner. Naturally I will omit dessert today, and will have no more than one piece of bread. I plan these things this way *today* because this is the best way for me to live. I am a compulsive overeater and always will be. Therefore my meal planning is vital if I am to retain my health and my sanity.

I could care less about my doctor's set of expectations for my future weight. It isn't important. If I lose ten or twelve more pounds, it will doubtless please both of us. But I'm not going to get hung up over it. I'll do today only those things that need doing. Today is sufficient unto itself.

If you think you can live on a future plan whereby you calculate how much weight you will lose each month for the next year or two, lots of luck. I wish you well. You can do something I can't do and obviously you have more will power, or whatever in hell they call it, than I have. I've gone that route before, I've tried it, and it just doesn't work for me. I do my thing the way I've found best for me—one day at a time—and you do things your way.

But if it isn't working for you, why not try my way? Try living your life, abstaining from compulsive overeating, one day at a time. It works. I don't know why it works. But it works.

If you are familiar with Alcoholics Anonymous, you may already know that alcoholics are living their lives *one day at a time*. I didn't invent this philosophy; the founders of Alcoholics Anonymous did. The alcoholic and the compulsive overeater are brothers and sisters under the skin, both driven by a baffling, powerful obsession they do not understand and cannot control. The alcoholic on the program maintains sobriety by living life *one day at a time*, abstaining from alcohol *today*.

My friends in our local chapter of Overeaters Anonymous live that way too: by abstaining from compulsive overeating *one day at a time*.

65

Can a person *really* live life this way? One day at a time? Certainly one can. But what about financial decisions? What about my job . . . my business?

The problems that need solving come up one day at a time. Let us say my stockbroker calls and suggests a change in my portfolio—buying or selling. I may make a decision today. I may also ask him, today, to gather more information on which to base my decision. When that information arrives, it won't be tomorrow—it will be *today*. Your job may call for future planning, making projections, deciding the shape of things to come. But what you do is *today* work. You can't do yesterday's work today; that's gone. Impossible. And nobody can do tomorrow's work. That's for tomorrow . . . when it will be today. If a man comes to sell you insurance on your life, perhaps, or an annuity for your child's education, you make the decision, pro or con, on the appointed day: today.

"But the way you talk, you say every day is today." Certainly. That's the whole point. Quit mourning for lost yesterdays and worrying yourself fat over tomorrows. Just live today, one day at a time.

This is our next step:

Resolve that from now on you are going to live your life one day at a time. Decide today, just for today, to eat three nutritious, well-balanced meals that you will plan in advance, today.

By three nutritious, well-balanced meals. I mean meals that are good for *you*.

And further resolve, just for today, that you will take nothing between meals except low-calorie beverages and will refrain from compulsive overeating. Just for today.

TEN
ooooooooooo

The Lord is my Shepherd, I shall not want.

Except for my father's funeral and the weddings of my two daughters, I have not been in a church for sixteen years. When I was a smallish boy I attended Sunday school. I don't know if they still do this in churches today, but back then we were given a little cardboard box designed to look like a treasure chest containing a set of printed envelopes, one for each Sunday of the church school year. Every Sunday morning I would stand before my father for inspection, suited, necktied, spit-combed, and shoe-shined. After I had been sent back to correct whatever didn't pass my father's eagle eye (like washing my neck), he would take my church envelope and ceremoniously insert a shiny quarter for the collection. But if I was very careful, I could undo one corner of the glued flap just enough to get the quarter out. Then I would substitute a dime, feeling that God wouldn't really be all that offended.

When Sunday school was out, I would hurry my bicycle (a brown and white Ranger, if you remember those days) down three blocks to the drugstore. In that long-ago depression era, fifteen cents would buy a boy the most delicious ice-cream soda you ever saw. (Weep, you kids of the seventies. They made them with three scoops of real ice cream and real chocolate.)

What I was doing was compulsively overeating with God's money.

High school rather finished me on religion. My parents shipped me to a four-year military academy where we had compulsory chapel every Sunday morning. We were marched in at strict attention; then à la West Point, we plebes (first-year cadets) were made to sit rigidly, backs like ramrods, on the front two inches of hard pew seats for the entire service. My cadet commander was there. The commandant and the superintendent were there. But whether God was there or not I've never been certain.

I did get religion of a sort for a few years when I was in my thirties: became a vestryman, passed the plate, the whole trip. But one day I had a very serious question to ask the minister about my conduct and my life. What I decided about our conversation was something like this: that minister may have been speaking about God, but I don't think God was speaking through him. That's harsh, I know. Possibly I was wrong. But I don't think so.

Then I began some postgraduate work at the University of California in anthropology and sociology. To seriously analyze religion, per se, is to build yourself a very large impediment toward religion. I didn't exactly consider myself an atheist, you understand, but I could never take the Bible literally.

There is one story, however, that disturbs me greatly. It seems two prospectors, a Christian and an atheist, were talking together at the bar of an Alaskan saloon.

"Haven't you ever," asked the Christian, "haven't you ever in your entire life needed God desperately and prayed to Him for help?"

The other man thought awhile. "Yes," he said slowly, "last winter. I was stuck up in Whitehorse Pass, it was sixty-five below zero, my sled dogs had died, I was out of food, and I was completely lost. I knew I was a goner unless help arrived. So I prayed to your God—I prayed as hard as I could."

"What happened?"

"Nothing at all. Didn't do a damn bit of good!"

"But my God, man. You're *here!* He must have heard your prayer and rescued you after all."

"No such thing," said the atheist. "Some old Eskimo came along with his dog team and gave me a ride back home."

The thing about that story is that Eskimos have been arriving in my life lately from the strangest directions and always when I need them the most.

Dr. Frank was my first Eskimo, but I didn't know it at the time. I honestly thought he was another doctor, perhaps better than the rest, but just another doctor with a drawerful of diet sheets. I knew Dr. Frank was an alcoholic and active in Alcoholics Anonymous, but I hadn't had any experience with AA people and had never been exposed to what AA's call "tough love." Dr. Frank told me I had severe diabetes and severe hypertension and was grossly obese.

I knew *that.*

Then he told me he was putting me on a diet.

I figured *that.* I told him it wouldn't work. I told him I had gone on and off diets for years. I told him I had no will power, that I couldn't live on 900 calories a day, that "I really didn't eat very much," and so on.

"Then get the hell out of my office and die," Dr. Frank said. "I'll not sign your death certificate. Get yourself some quack to do it. I don't give a goddamn if you live or die. I'm a busy man and I've got better things to do than waste time talking to you."

Tough love. But that's when something, I don't know what, some small voice, told me to tell Dr. Frank I was like an alcoholic: a compulsive overeater.

"Sweet Jesus," muttered Dr. Frank. And he whistled low and mournful. "But you have to eat, don't you? You're an alcoholic about food. God. If I had to drink it would kill me."

What Dr. Frank did was to put me on a "diet," but a different kind of diet from anything I had ever heard of before. I was a diabetic, a so-called mature-onset diabetic. A diabetic of normal weight must still follow a diet in order to control his sugar intake in line with the number of units of insulin he shoots. My goal weight, according to Dr. Frank, was 175 pounds. And a 175-pound man requires about 2,750 calories a day in order to sustain his weight, assuming he exercises moderately and his metabolism is normal. Dr. Frank placed me on the diet recommended by the American Diabetes Association: 2,725 calories with a bias toward high protein, less fat, and less carbohydrate. (In nutritional terms, about protein, 125 grams; fat, 125 grams; carbohydrate, 275 grams.)

Since the arrival of my first Eskimo my weight has dropped from 276 to 185, my waist from size 50 to size 36, my blood pressure from 210/170 to 120/70, and my sugar count from 445 to 94. I owe my life, my health, and my sanity to an Eskimo named Dr. Frank. (Since "Dr. Frank" is an anonymous alcoholic and rather modest to boot, I will refrain from telling you his last name. If I did, he would hang a Gaelic curse on me and I would turn into a spotted toad.)

Marianne was my second Eskimo. By the end of July, under Dr. Frank's patient regime, I had lost 35 pounds but my old craving to overeat compulsively was still there and growing worse instead of better. The diet I was on was restoring my health but not my sanity. I was in the black pit. I knew . . . I knew . . . from bitter, painful experience repeated over and over, that I was on the verge of blowing my diet.

The classified section of our daily newspaper, in the "Personals" column, has a small, two-line advertisement that runs daily.

OVEREATERS ANONYMOUS
343-2267

I guess I had seen the ad before, probably many times, but it had never registered. What the hell. I had nothing to lose.

The phone buzzed three times, then a soft feminine voice answered. "My name is Marianne. Can I help you?"

I briefly told her why I had called: that I was having trouble staying on my diet.

"We aren't a diet club. We are a group of compulsive overeaters," she told me. "Are you just trying to lose a few pounds or do you have a history of compulsive overeating?"

"My God," I said. I almost cried with relief. "Marianne, I think I've found a home."

Marianne gave me the meeting times and places where two chapters of Overeaters Anonymous met on a weekly basis in private conference rooms donated by a local hospital: one on Thursday evenings at 8:00 P.M. and the other on Saturday afternoons at 3:00 P.M. I attended my first OA meeting on Saturday. As I walked in the door, a thin woman moved grace-fully toward me.

"George—I'm Marianne. Welcome."

Marianne, I learned, had been a member of Overeaters An-noymous for just over five years. When she first entered OA, Marianne weighed something in excess of 350 pounds. (Her doctor's scale went only to 350; the pointer was rigidly stuck at the top.) During her first two years her weight dropped to 105 pounds, where it stands at the present time. Her weight has not fluctuated more than a pound or so since. Her appear-ance is perfectly "normal" for her height and bone structure. Her face shows the muscular tightness of a girl who exercises and bicycles regularly. She wears fashionable clothes with flair.

"My name is Marianne. I am a compulsive overeater."

She introduced me to the other compulsive overeaters at the meeting, using only the first names of each. She explained that last names, occupations, and personal details about members are never revealed. Some of the members were thin, as thin as Marianne. Others were fat. Most were in-betweens. I shook hands with each member and was given literature from a table. It explained that Overeaters Anonymous was an offshoot of Alcoholics Anonymous and that the same meeting format and the same principles could be found in either organization. Sev-eral of the members said they were both alcoholics *and* com-pulsive overeaters. The meeting began:

"God grant us the serenity to accept the things we cannot change, the courage to change the things we can, and the wis-dom to know the difference." In unison we recited the alco-holics' and the compulsive overeaters' prayer. Not one night has passed since that I have not said this simple prayer before going to sleep.

The meeting had a strangely religious flavor I had not expected to encounter, although it certainly bore no resemblance to any church service I had ever attended and had no connection with any organized church. Members kept talking about something they called their "Higher Power." Frankly, I was puzzled. The phrase kept coming back. "Higher Power."

Yes . . . I could admit to myself there was a "Higher Power." I wasn't necessarily willing to call *It* God.

"You don't have to," one of the members told me. "I call mine 'Harold.' You know: 'Our Father who art in heaven, Harold be Thy name.' . . . I call Him *Harold*."

The second and third steps of Alcoholics (and Overeaters) Anonymous that members are asked to take are these:

> *We came to believe that a Power greater than ourselves could restore us to sanity.*

> *We made a decision to turn our will and our lives over to the care of God as we understood him.*

And the eleventh and twelfth steps:

> *We sought through prayer and meditation to improve our conscious contact with God as we understood Him, praying only for knowledge of His will for us and the power to carry that out.*

> *Having had a spiritual awakening as the results of these steps, we tried to carry this message to all compulsive overeaters, and to practice these principles in all our affairs.*[1]

I found this strange, but not difficult. It works. I pride my-

---

[1] *Alcoholics Anonymous* (Alcoholics Anonymous World Services, Inc., third edition, 1976), pp. 59, 60.

self on being a pragmatic person. Whatever works, works. It works for me, therefore for me it's okay.

A few days later I was faced with the kind of business problem calculated to send any normal person into a black fit of depression and a frustrated compulsive overeater into the bakery. This time I hesitated, put the bad news down on my desk, and thought.

"God grant me the serenity to accept the things I cannot change." Okay . . . what category did this problem fit? Could I change anything *today* or not? No! I could not. It was the kind of problem without an immediate solution. Then I took the next step.

"God," I asked quietly, "give me the serenity to accept this thing I cannot change. God . . . I can't handle this. It is going to eat me alive. Please, sir . . . *you* handle it for me."

And you know what? He did. The problem hasn't gone away; it still exists and I still can't do anything to change it. But it doesn't bug me. God (or whoever He is) is handling it for me. I asked Him for serenity. He gives me serenity.

I don't try to cope with my feelings about compulsive overeating any more. I ask God or my Higher Power or Harold or Whatever I'm talking to, whatever It is, to handle the problem, and He does.

This is our next step:

You handle the little day-to-day problems one day at a time. Let God or your Higher Power handle the big ones you cannot solve. If you ask Him for serenity, courage, and wisdom, He will grant them to you, no strings attached. Trust Him. It works.

ELEVEN

> I awoke one morning and found myself free from the
> dreadful slavery of overeating.
>
> —Marianne

Maybe it's because those fourteen-day grapefruit diets are so
basically miserable, but a lot of normal-thin friends treat me as
if I were heroic. Sheer nonsense. If you really want to be thin,
are willing to go to any lengths to be thin, and are willing to
say out loud in public that you are a compulsive overeater,
then the only heroic thing you will ever do in the program is
already accomplished. That first step—saying you are a compulsive overeater—is the tough part.

I hadn't really leveled with myself for so many years I just
wasn't ready to see myself as I really was: an obsessive/com-
pulsive fat man with an eating problem. It's hard, friend.

One of my best friends in this entire world is in a conva-
lescent hospital back East dying from booze. His wife called

me last night. Bill's liver is about gone. His head is connected by tubes to some kind of machine. He thinks he is on a train, taking a nice ride. I asked an AA mutual friend of ours why Bill never joined Alcoholics Anonymous.

"You got to hit bottom," he said. "Bill never hit bottom."

"But, God, Bill's dying. Isn't that enough?"

"No. . . . Bill never hit bottom. He could never bring himself to say he was an alcoholic. Bill had too much pride to save his life."

"Candy is dandy but liquor is quicker." I don't think so. A lot of alcoholics manage to hold down good jobs and circulate in society for years and years before the stuff finally catches up with them. A fat compulsive overeater can't hide very well in a size-52 suit. I admit I hit bottom that day in Dr. Frank's office, but I was in trouble for years and years and everybody knew it except me. For more than fifteen of those years I was president of a midwestern food company owned by myself and other members of my family. Nobody ever told the boss he was too fat. But one day we sold the company to a large corporation and I hit the employment lines for the first time in my life. And I learned what it is to be a fat man looking for a big-money job.

"Don't call us, we'll call you." "I don't think we have anything here that would interest you." "I don't see how you could help us at this time." "We have several other candidates to interview. If we have anything, we'll let you know."

I could see "fat man" all over their faces.

So guess what I did about it? Of course. I got fatter.

I had enough money to buy a large life insurance annuity to protect my family and provide for our old age, as they say in the ads. The salesman was delighted to write the contract. But I couldn't pass the physical. Hell . . . I bet if I'd been a secret alcoholic or sex pervert they would have sold me the insurance. And I'd have gotten one of those jobs. But I was fat. And fatter. And my eating got worse.

When Alcoholics Anonymous was first established, during its early years most of the members were men. Maybe women didn't drink as much as men or, more likely, women just weren't about to admit they had a drinking problem. That's changed now. But at the present time more women than men seem willing to say they are compulsive overeaters and to join organizations like Overeaters Anonymous. I doubt if the distribution of fat varies all that much by sex. Maybe men suffer from false pride, as women alcoholics did once. Maybe men can survive better in a thin world than women. But I don't think so. I suspect Winston Churchill would have one devil of a time being elected Prime Minister in the era of television, to say nothing of a man as fat as William Howard Taft. Those days are over. Today the fashion trends more toward Shakespeare's villain Cassius, he of the "lean and hungry look."

(If you want to know if this is a thin world or not, just try buying a pair of Levi's, size 48.)

One of my friends got started recently on kind of an unusual new career: this guy is a professional fly-fishing expert who teaches classes in fly fishing on trout streams to groups of well-heeled businessmen and arranges trout-fishing trips for them to exotic spots like New Zealand and Argentina. But the guy is fat, a compulsive overeater, and the way he's blowing up, he just doesn't make it. He isn't getting the TV appearances he needs for public relations. Fat him just doesn't somehow look right on one of those rugged trout streams. To tell you the truth, the guy is beginning to look like Yogi Bear with a fly rod in his paw.

You know about obesity. Like me, you've read the handouts

on your doctor's coffee table and the *Reader's Digest* horror stories. Sure. Fat and hypertension go together like ham and eggs. And, friend, diabetes is the toast on the side. (Doctors told me this for years. I didn't believe them. I was wrong.) I can tell you more about so-called mature-onset diabetes than you want to know. Your mouth gets dry as a desert. Bone-dry. So dry, your tongue cracks. You crave cold, sweet liquids. You pour beer, colas, and pop down your throat. The more sugar you take, the worse the diabetes, and the more sugar you crave, the more you drink, round and round, round and round, worse and worse. You get open sores all over your skin. Bruises don't heal. Your kidneys are messed up. You get up to urinate five or six times or more a night. And you sweat. God, how you sweat. And if you are staying away from food control or an organization like Overeaters Anonymous because you are too damn proud-male to admit you need help, let me tell you mature-onset diabetes really screws up your love life, friend. You just don't erect right. And maybe you never will again. (This is no bull. Believe me.)

The United States Navy has a special program for officers and enlisted men they call "shipshape." ("Shape up or ship out!") At just one naval base here in California they have five separate chapters of Overeaters Anonymous. As we all know, corporations have finally gotten smart about alcoholism, a problem costing industry billions of dollars each year in absenteeism, lost careers, and just plain trouble. Obesity costs money, too. Maybe your company should investigate a "shipshape" program of its own. As they say, it's a matter of dollars and sense.

The Overeaters Anonymous program probably isn't the only hope for compulsive overeaters, but it is the one I'm the most familiar with and basically its program embraces nearly all the ideas we've discussed in this book. More important, it exists in most every medium-size and large city in America. (Los Angeles had fifty-one chapters at last count.) OA hasn't had the publicity that AA has had so far, but the word is getting around. If you are interested, check your daily newspaper for a small ad listing a number to call, or contact your local community service bureau or your local "hot line," or call the local Alcoholics Anonymous contact phone number. At last resort, call or write Overeaters Anonymous, 2190 190th Street, Torrance, California 90504; (213) 320-7941.

If all else fails, ask how you can start a chapter of your own. That's how new chapters get started. That's how Overeaters Anonymous grows. The OA World Service people at the address above will help you get started and send you any literature or information you may need. And after you take the step and join, keep coming back. Keep coming back. And again . . . keep coming back. It works.

No one quite seems to understand why the relationship between Alcoholics Anonymous and the medical profession has been so tenuous. One of the three founders of AA was a physician. Perhaps doctors think AA and OA are in competition with them; I don't know. (A large alcoholic "drying-out" sanitarium in my community is owned by a group of physicians.) But if you are a physician or psychiatrist or psychologist with obese patients and you are interested in the material discussed in this book, I'm certain Overeaters Anonymous would be happy to supply you and your fellow physicians with further literature and information. (It can't hurt to find out, now, can it?)

Overeaters Anonymous is not a "diet club." No discussion of food is allowed at meetings, no recipes for low-cal fudge or brownies. No scales. No competition over who loses or gains what or how much. Some members are fat, some medium, and some quite svelt. Some have become members *after* going on a "diet" and losing substantial amounts of weight: scared to death they are about to start eating compulsively again.

The key concept of Overeaters Anonymous, as I understand the program, is the word *abstinence:* a rough equivalent of the Alcoholics Anonymous word *sobriety.* Abstinence, the way OA uses the term, is approximately what we have been talking about throughout this book. *Abstinence is not a diet. It is a plan for living with food.* Abstinence is eating three pre-planned, nourishing meals a day (nourishing for *you*) with no snacks in between meals, no eating of former binge foods, and nothing outside these three meals except low-cal or no-cal beverages such as coffee, tea, and no-cal sodas. (As you can see, an abstinence diet is whatever works for *you.*) You plan your abstinence diet with the help of a sponsor, a member of your chapter who has kept his or her abstinence for a considerable length of time. And you live this way, *one day at a time,* with the help of your Higher Power or whatever you wish to call God.

So abstinence is not a diet. It is a way of life, designed for and by you, that will enable you to live in a new way without compulsive overeating. *Abstinence is a radical redesign of your life.*

Nobody can live the rest of their life on a "diet." But an alcoholic (there are no *ex*-alcoholics) can maintain sobriety for life. And a compulsive overeater (there are no *ex*-compulsive overeaters, either) *can* maintain abstinence for life.

It was hard, hard, hard at first. I went through hell the first week. It was hell because I was still insane with the craving to eat. Then, suddenly, it was easier. And easier yet. I am still a compulsive overeater and always will be, but for more than a year I have maintained my abstinence, one day at a time. What was strange torture has now become a way of life. I think my personality has changed, too. At least, people tell me it has. I seem to be softer now, more loving perhaps, certainly more tolerant of myself and others around me.

If life has been a stage and we the actors on that stage, I have played the role of critic to the play. I remember the days in my company presidency when I played the role of chief bastard: the critic of the foibles of everyone around me. But that's over now, thank God. Everyone I meet seems so much nicer. Maybe it's me. I hope so.

One man was asked why he started attending meetings of Overweight Anonymous. "Oh," he muttered, looking at the pretty girls in the group, "in the beginning it was to lose weight and maybe get laid. But I kept coming back to get sane."

Another man told me a story about the time he and a friend of his drove to the race track at Santa Anita to pick up another friend's horse trailer and expensive race horse. They were driving back down the freeway, towing the horse and trailer, and the driver was going about thirty-six miles an hour while people kept passing them at seventy.

"How come you're driving so slowly?" the passenger asked.

"Don't you realize that horse back there is worth over $100,000?"

"But, my God," he screamed at the driver, "what about me? *What about me?*"

My next-door neighbor has a fancy show dog that has won about every dog show it has ever been entered in. What do you think my neighbors feed that dog? And what do you think they feed their children?

A sociology teacher I once had gave a lecture about "people

as objects." He said people treated people as objects: valuable objects, loving objects, hated objects, even sometimes useful objects. I know a lot of businessmen who treat their employees as useful objects. Some mothers treat their daughters as useful objects. They want them to make a good (rich) marriage, to be active in the Junior League, to have a "good address" (expensive home), and to be in the society columns so mother can bask in the reflected glory of her daughter.

I think my mother and father tended to treat me as a valuable object: as the successor to run the family business and therefore of potential value, an object to fatten up after sickness, to educate for future use.

What kind of object do you see yourself as? For years and years I was the most hated object I knew. That was my insanity. I was the most dreadful, fat object in the world.

I think, for maybe the first time in my life, that I love myself. I know some people think that's wrong, to love oneself, but it seems to me that in loving myself more, I'm beginning to love other people too. And that can't be so bad, can it? I can honestly say I like my thin self. And finally I'm beginning to like other thin men and women. I cherish my body now. (I have a few soft fat rolls here and there. But I can live with them. Charles Atlas I ain't, nor Paul Newman either. But I'll settle for *me*.) And as I love and cherish myself, I love and cherish all of you, fat and thin alike. That's what I mean by sanity.

God . . . thank you for the serenity to accept the things I cannot change, the courage to change the things I can . . . and the wisdom to know the difference.

TWELVE

○○○○○○○○○○○○○○○○○○○○

I fear for my wife's sanity, I really do. Just a minute ago I told her I was going to include a chapter on physical fitness in this book and now she's doubled up on the floor in fits of laughter. She says maybe I should write about something I understand, like nuclear energy or astrophysics. Betty says my writing about physical fitness is like a professional football player's doing a book on ballet.

"I think you're wrong," I told her. "Compulsive overeaters like me have been getting lectured to by thin gym teachers all our lives. It's time fats talked to fats about fat."

Speaking of football players, do you know what happens to them when they retire from football and start to add inches around the waist? If you say they gain weight—wrong! They *lose* weight. Muscle tissue weighs considerably more than fat. For example, the Los Angeles Rams have a guard who is more or less typical of professional linemen: he is 6'2" tall, weighs 254 pounds, and has a 31" waist and a 22" neck! Your doctor's chart for a man 6′2″ gives his "normal" weight as about 187. Medically he is 67 pounds overweight. Actually he probably doesn't have a pick of fat on him, not with that 31″ waist. But if he retires from football and takes the kind of sedentary desk job most of us have, he'd better plan on losing most of those 67 pounds or else he will be fat.

You may remember the old "Charles Atlas" ads aimed at the "97-pound weakling" market. The whole idea was to gain a substantial amount of weight by building muscle.

When young men join the army and go through basic training—twenty-five-mile hikes, close-order drill, obstacle courses, and lots of running, accompanied by a 4,000-calorie-plus daily food intake—the fat recruits lose weight and the thin gain. They equalize.

Your best, most consistent guide to your weight isn't your scale, although your scale weight helps advise you on the progress of your abstinence. The best guide is your tape measure, applied periodically to your waistline. If your waistline grows bigger, you have gained fat no matter what your scale says.

(My doctor tells me this doesn't work 100 percent for the ladies. He says you should clutch yourself some skin just above and to the left of your navel. If it measures more than an inch in thickness, you are definitely on the fatty side.)

Because exercise adds weight (via new muscle tissue) a regular fitness program can be threatening to dieters. One time I joined one of those Weight Watchers-type diet clubs, the kind they operate for a profit, and the first thing our fearless leader told us was to refrain from any unusual amount of added exercise while we were on his "program."

"If you start exercising," he said, "you are going to be disappointed in your weight loss."

Well . . . maybe so. Most all of us have had the experience of exercising strenuously and finding, to our sorrow, that we have gained weight rather than lost. So don't exercise if you are just interested in your scale and not in your health or your waistline measurements. But if you want to avoid stretch marks and don't like hanging folds of skin that feel like a dead chicken to the touch, read on.

No one hates exercise and exercising more than I. My hero used to be the famous drama critic Alexander Woollcott, who said he got his exercise acting as pall bearer for his friends who exercised. Time was when I got a big laugh out of that line. But alas, the late Mr. Woollcott died of the complications of his obesity, and one presumes *his* pallbearers were men who exercised.

I previously mentioned attending a military school during my high school years. Any inclination I ever had toward athletics and physical fitness disappeared in that place. The first thing they did was put me on the "diet table," an extremely humiliating and degrading experience for a young boy: a stigma that loudly and clearly meant "fat" to others and, even more important, to myself. If I hadn't known I was a fat boy before, I did then. Second, they placed me in a special physical training group consisting of the halt, the lame, the near-blind, and the fat like me. It was dreadful. The school's motives were good, I suppose. But being on the diet table and in the special physical education group set us apart from other boys our age. We were marked for special treatment, which unfortunately also included special hazing, special cruelty, even special brutality.

As I remember, they did dangle a kind of plum in front of us. Each June the school gave a medal to the boy showing "the greatest physical improvement" for the year. I had shrunk a total of 39 pounds and lost out to a boy who had taken off 41. That I can still remember the specifics after all those years is indicative of how I felt. As the other boy came forward for his medal, I decided then and there that my days of being pushed around were over. They could make me attend classes, they could make me salute, they could make me attend chapel and march in formation, but there was no way under heaven they could make me lose weight or stop eating compulsively if I didn't want to. My stubbornness paid off. I gained back the 39 pounds and added 30 more, and eating became entrenched in my mind, engraved in my head, as the one best way of getting back at authority.

I became a rebel and overeating compulsively was the way I set out on the road. God help me, that's exactly what I did!

Everybody in that military school was supposed to go out for athletics. It was a very, very jock-oriented place. My sophomore year I went out for the wrestling team (as a heavyweight, naturally) and broke my collarbone. The following year I tried boxing until a budding young Muhammad Ali type broke my nose. Then my senior year I joined the varsity football team and managed to break something in my left hand, ruin a knee, and break my nose again, twice. That kind of did it, folks. I graduated and left for college, and when the freshman football coach at Iowa State tried to draft me for his team, I flat-out refused. The remainder of my college months after Pearl Harbor and before my draft number came up were spent pleasantly drinking beer and luring coeds out on blanket parties.

You understand I was fat, of course, that first year of college. I weighed about 238, as I remember. But God, I was strong. I had muscles on top of muscles, the kind of good-old-boy belly you could hit with a baseball bat without making a dent. But when I finally woke up, I was fifty-two years old, hypertensive, and diabetic, and I weighed 276. I didn't have those muscles any more. I was just plain hog fat.

The more obese a man or woman becomes, the slower he or she moves, and the harder it is to get any exercise. The blanket of fat over the rib cage makes breathing more difficult. In extreme obesity even moderate movement causes lack of breath. Climbing a flight of stairs becomes major work. If you take a pair of suitcases, load 30 pounds of books in each, and carry them up a flight of stairs, you approximate the effort a man or woman who is 60 pounds overweight must put out. The entire process of gaining weight is a self-defeating, vicious circle.

When you go on your personal abstinence program and begin eating three normal meals a day, you reverse the process. The more weight you lose on abstinence, the better you feel, the faster you move, the easier that stair climb becomes. The vicious circle is reversed. Instead of just barely moving, you really *move*. Those flat feet and tired old legs suddenly feel like wire springs.

But as you lose fat, your skin crinkles and begins to hang in ugly folds. Your view of yourself in the mirror isn't as rewarding as you might like. This is where exercise comes in: rears its ugly head, as it were. Hate it or not, my personal abstinence program includes *moderate* exercise.

By moderate I mean this: enough work performed to make me out of breath for approximately one minute; enough to raise my pulse to a count of about 120 beats per minute; enough work to make my muscles hurt. The first time you do five deep knee bends you may be out of breath, have an elevated pulse, and hurt all over. But after a week or so, five deep knee bends may do little or nothing. So . . . keep going. Go until you really hurt. Add new exercises, eliminate the easy ones. It won't be long until you positively amaze yourself.

The key to my personal exercise program is walking. *Don't* try jogging. Not yet. You'll probably kill yourself trying to jog. If just going for a walk sounds like a drag, try turning walking into a necessity. One way is to get yourself a dog that needs walking, too. Not a silly poodle-type dog: a walking dog like a German shepherd or a Labrador—a dog that really walks. Another way is to leave your car in the garage or the parking lot. I have an old habit of taking morning and afternoon coffee at a cafe four blocks away. By leaving my car in the lot, I get an eight-block walk twice each day. In my fat days I ate lunch at a place across the street from my office: the kind of restaurant that features high-calorie cheeseburgers, greasy french fries, and rubber pie. Now I walk five blocks to a tiny restaurant that serves salads, home-baked whole wheat bread, and good soup. My lunchtime calorie intake is cut by two thirds, and I get the ten-block walk as a bonus. Adding it all up, I walk twenty-six blocks each day instead of driving the car. That's over two miles.

(And when you walk, for heaven's sake, folks, *walk!* Swing your arms. Put some spring in your step. Make those calves hurt. You can make a four-block walk quite a punishing experience if you really stride out.)

My walking gets faster every day now—and easier. What I'm doing now is running one block and walking the next in alternation. Maybe people think I'm nuts. They do smile, but I kind of think they're smiling with me, not at me. At least, I hope so.

My second form of exercise is what I like to call the "physical jerks," in British army style, instead of calisthenics, which it really is. (I hate calisthenics, so I changed the name.) I do all the usual body-bending, hands-to-floor touching, knee bends, and the rest. I found conventional push-ups to be quite punishing and developed some bad back pains. A little book I'd heartily recommend called *Total Fitness in 30 Minutes a Week*,[1] by Laurence E. Morehouse and Leonard Gross, has a good suggestion. Step back about a stride from a counter (your kitchen counter is about the right height) and place your palms face down and far enough apart to be comfortable. Now keep your back straight and support your weight on your palms. You can do quite nice push-ups this way and, by varying your distance and speed, you can make them as easy or as difficult as you wish. It takes a bit of experimentation and is hard to describe, but these modified push-ups work quite nicely. By the way, Morehouse and Gross are the inventors of the pulse rate system of checking your exercise. They developed an exercising machine (a kind of bicycle, I guess) for astronauts to use in deep space. The astronaut's pulse rate automatically feeds back to the machine and thus varies the resistance of the pedals, keeping the pulse rate/resistance factor at about 120 beats per minute. This way the number of minutes each spends on the machine is constant, but the work output necessary to pedal varies according to his physical condition.

Just keep in mind that your "physical jerks" should make you out of breath, should speed your pulse to about 120, and should hurt a bit. If you don't feel the pain, it don't mean a thing.

I haven't mentioned competitive sports such as golf, tennis, and handball for a variety of reasons. Time was when I played a lot of golf, but I find golf more frustrating than exercising.

[1] New York: Simon & Schuster, 1975; and New York: Pocket Books, 1976.

And when I get frustrated, I want to eat. If you're fifty or more pounds overweight and haven't been doing much exercising, tennis or handball could quite literally be the death of you. Take it easy. Everything in moderation, one day at a time.

Swimming is wonderful exercise if you really swim laps instead of floating peacefully around in the pool. Trouble is, most backyard pools aren't big enough for lap swimming and the YMCA-type pool requires a lot of time off each day, locker room changing, and so on. For me, doing laps is dreadfully boring and I tend to end up floating around like a wounded whale. But if it suits you, fine. I haven't really been on a bicycle since I was thirteen. It seems to me to be a normal thins' game, but if the seat fits you, by all means ride it. Naturally, all this depends on how overweight you really are, what kind of condition you are in, your age, blood pressure, and so forth. You and your physician need to confer about this, by all means. If you haven't played tennis for twenty years, though, I doubt if he'll be very enthusiastic.

The best thing about exercise as part of your personal abstinence program is that it makes you feel good all over. You look much better in the mirror. Your tummy goes flat. If you are a male, you lose your boobies; and if of the female sex, they become more upstanding and outstanding. Your ass gets nice and flat. (My daughter says I have "nice buns," whatever precisely *that* means.) And finally, weight reduction and moderate exercise make you screw good—a calorie-burning exercise in itself.

How much time should you devote to exercise? That depends. Enough to make you feel good without its becoming a crashing bore. You are your own best judge of how much time to spend. Like everything else we have recommended, do it *one day at a time*. Remember the three key principles: first, exercise should be hard enough to make you out of breath for about one minute; second, exercise to raise your pulse moderately to about 120 beats per minute; and last, exercise should hurt good all over. The more you exercise on a regular program, the harder and harder you will have to push yourself to satisfy these three criteria. Keep it up.

This is our last step: *include regular daily exercise as part of your food abstinence program.*

THIRTEEN

ooooooooooooooooooooooooooo

I have been a grossly obese person most of my life. Doctors tell me they know of no disease more baffling than obesity. Being fat has wrecked my life and my health. What I contend is this: obesity is not a disease in the classic medical sense but a baffling compulsion arising out of social/psychological factors derived from the patient's childhood experiences. Basically, obesity is a symptom of a response to frustration: a compulsion to overeat.

Obesity is also a self-confirming prophecy: once a child is labeled "fat" by his or her peer group (labeled *deviant* in the classic sociological sense of the word) the child accepts his or her perceived role as genuine and self-labels him- or herself as deviant-fat. Once formed in childhood, these ego images are difficult if not impossible to alter in later life. The primary point of difficulty is the utter inability of the individual on a classic medical "diet" to perceive of him- or herself as "thin," no matter what the scale indicates.

The medical practitioner is viewed by the obese patient as another threatening normal-thin authority figure. His demands on the patient seem frustrating and frightening; therefore the natural tendency of the patient placed on a classic medical diet is to protect him- or herself by overeating compulsively: the very thing the diet is designed to stop. Further, the obese patient tends to be obsessively goal-oriented, future-oriented, filled with guilt for past misdeeds, and perfection-oriented as well. The classic "authority-patient" relationship tends to increase this problem.

Physicians view obesity in a simplistic fashion. A symptom —obesity—is defined as a "disease" in the formal medical sense rather than taken for what it is: a perceived phenomenon of a highly complex social/psychological nature. Classic low-calorie diets only reduce the immediate symptom without alleviating the underlying cause. Further treatment (amphetamines, for example) simply complicates the matter and very likely endangers the patient.

Psychological methods have failed as utterly as the medical. They fail because the problem of confrontation between a normal-thin practitioner and his obese patient is but a re-enactment of the thin versus fat world the patient has been living in. Group therapy fails as well unless the group members are *all* compulsive overeaters. Skinnerian reward/punishment psychology I would reject out of hand, not on the basis that it might not work, but rather because small-animal training methods repel me. They are repugnant if workable—indefensible if plausible. Brainwashing is not an acceptable solution to human misery.

Diets are designed by normal-thin nutritionists for normal-thin people with small amounts of weight to lose. On a long-time basis (for gross obesity) low-calorie diets bring on frustration problems without denting the capacity of the patient to overeat compulsively. Extreme medical methods such as intestinal resection, wiring the jaws shut, or severe fasting under hospital supervision reduce the symptom (the obesity) but fail to eliminate the original compulsion to overeat.

Compulsive overeaters share certain qualities: they tend to be bright, above-average people; they have common histories of obese childhoods; they have repeatedly attempted to diet, only to regain the previous weight and more; and they have common ego images as self-hateful objects of little or no worth. Compulsive overeaters commonly form strong dependency relationships with normal thins: relationships that are threatened when the overeater diets and loses weight. Most of all, compulsive overeaters are simply people who overeat compulsively. We do not know why . . . the devil makes us do it.

In this we are like alcoholics, kleptomaniacs, sex perverts, and other compulsively driven people. We are victims of something we do not understand. It is too much for us. So, in extreme frustration, I overeat. My God, it is the only way I know to kill the pain in my head. And having glutted myself, I hate myself even more than before. So I eat.

Doctors, by words and action, tell me I am a hateful object. Instead of making my head better, they make it worse. They say I have no will power. But, God—I know *that*.

Fat people spend all their lives in a world of thin people and with rare exceptions make no friends with the fat-like-them. Thus the obese cut themselves off from the only group of people who share common feelings of self-hate and self-doubt. Like the alcoholic, we keep our deviance secret, hidden away in our frustrated heads.

And there, right there, is the one possible solution. As alcoholic physicians will abundantly testify (one of the three

94

founders of AA was an alcoholic doctor), medical science has failed in the treatment and cure of alcoholism. "Drying out" no more cures alcoholism than "dieting" cures compulsive overeating. It is my contention that the method Alcoholics Anonymous pioneered many years ago is an acceptable treatment for compulsive overeating. I am not so naïve as to think it is the only possible answer. It may work wonders for some and utterly fail others. Neither do I expect physicians or psychologists to rush out and embrace this program, any more than they have supported Alcoholics Anonymous.

But I do know this. Last year I was in such a mess, physically and medically, that I didn't really care how I died. I was at rock bottom. I had no friends except my wife and children. I had lost the one last reflex of humanity: the will to live.

It seems like an almighty long and lonely distance from the bottom of my despair to the place where I stand so proudly. You're damn right I want to live! I like myself! I love myself! And I could never, never kill a thing I love.

These are the steps I took and this is how it works:

1. *Admit to yourself and to those nearest and dearest to you that you are a compulsive overeater.*

   I found that admitting the true nature of my problem, to myself and to others, was the first, vital step to sanity. Admitting I was a compulsive overeater changed my outlook on myself and gave me a start toward identification of my problems and acceptance of myself. I began to hate myself less and less once I had taken this first giant step to understanding.

2. *Understand that you do not need a deprivation diet to lose weight. If you eat the same diet as nor-*

mal thins, and exercise as much as they, you will eventually be a normal thin yourself.

Going on a "diet," per se, had never worked for me. I needed to change and modify my meals so that they were the same as those of a normal-thin person of my height, build, and metabolism and to learn to eat and live the life of a normal thin if I was to become one. From the beginning of my weight loss and continuing to this day, I eat three normal meals based on the caloric intake of a man my height. I am still a compulsive overeater and always will be, but I do not overeat compulsively.

3. *You cannot learn to be thin in a group of old thin friends, no matter how much they love you. You will always be their old fat friend.*

You can learn to be thin only among a group of fat friends and, by becoming thin, let them assign you the thin role.

My biggest problem involved in "dieting" and weight loss had always been that I did not "feel" thin, no matter what my scale said. I had learned, as a child, to play the fat role in the group. If I lost weight, I was always their fat friend on a diet. What you need is a warm circle of fat friends who can relate to one another. Overeaters Anonymous, a twig from the tree of Alcoholics Anonymous, is just such a group. You will find OA people to be warm, supportive, understanding, and honest with one another. Joining Overeaters Anonymous may be the best thing you have ever done in your entire life. Try it. The only thing you have to lose is your excess poundage. What you may very well gain is your health, your life, and wonderful new friends.

4. *Resolve that from now on you are going to live your life one day at a time. Decide today, just for today, to eat three nutritious, well-balanced meals that you will plan in advance, with no binge foods and nothing in between except low-calorie beverages.*

My past shames me and the future scares me. So I have decided deliberately to violate the most important precept of Western civilization and live my life just for today. I cannot possibly swear I will not eat compulsively tomorrow—or next year. But I can control today.

The food I eat TODAY will be nutritious and good for me, will taste good, and will be the right amount for a man of my stature.

5. *You handle the little day-to-day problems one day at a time. Let God or your Higher Power, whatever you wish to call Him, handle the big ones you cannot solve. If you ask Him for serenity, courage, and wisdom, He will grant them to you, no strings attached. Trust Him. It works.*

I'm not asking you to make a strange commitment. I am suggesting you may need help and strength as I did, do, need them. There are problems I simply can't handle alone. They make me frustrated. So I ask Him to help me through the day and He does. It works.

6. *Love yourself as you would expect others to love you.*

This was my insanity, that I was the most fat, most dreadful, most hated object I knew. This is what I mean by being insane. To be sane is to love oneself. As I was lacking in love for myself, so was I lacking in love for others.

If you handle the first five steps, this one will take care of itself. As you learn to love yourself, you will find others to love as well. And loving yourself means loving and cherishing your body. God made it. Love your body and love God.

7. *Include regular daily exercise as part of your food abstinence program. Abstinence is three normal, nourishing meals a day, one day at a time, under God's care, with regular exercise.*

Exercise is like brushing one's teeth. I don't particularly enjoy either one, but they're necessary. Exercise makes you feel good. When I look good and feel good, I like myself.

I have lived on my abstinence program for over a year. The mistakes or missteps I may have made in the past don't matter. I don't know if I'll be on the program next year. What I do know is that I am keeping my abstinence TODAY. That I can handle. So can you. If I can do it, so can you. Just for today.

I am awash in platitudes. Some of them are other-directed: from both thin and fat friends; some are inner-directed: from myself. My head is in a good place. I have enjoyed researching and writing this book. It may have been psychologically necessary for me to write about my baffling compulsion. In a sense (if you are acquainted with the Alcoholics Anonymous program, you will understand the term) this has been my "fearless moral inventory." Whatever it has been, I can sincerely say it has been personally satisfying.

I know from my own experience as well as the experiences of other compulsive overeaters that this program reflects truth and, most important, works. I make no claim to professional stature in any field, although I have taught college-level classes in sociology and social psychology. One thing continues to amaze me: I have searched the literature of medicine and psychiatry and a myriad of old and new books in the field of psychology without finding anything quite like the hypotheses herein presented. I am amazed because they sound quite simple and because so many lay people in Overeaters Anonymous groups throughout the country are following these same steps in a slightly altered but substantially similar fashion. That so many millions of alcoholics and compulsive overeaters have found help, love, and sanity and that their program is so ignored by professionals baffles me.

"Dr. Frank" has begun to counsel his obese patients in much the way I have described. I regret it seemed necessary for me to criticize the medical profession in this book. As I said in an earlier chapter, on three separate occasions doctors have saved my life with skill and devotion. But with all the research and great advances of medical science at their disposal, physicians haven't made a dent in the problem of obesity and compulsive overeating.

If this book makes sense to you, I hope you will share it with a friend, relative, spouse, or patient who is a compulsive overeater. We need to get our heads together and help people. That's the essence of loving: helping people. And if this helps you or your friend, then I have made a small payment on the huge debt I owe for my sanity and health. God love you.

References

Alcoholics Anonymous. 3rd. ed. New York: Alcoholics Anonymous World Services, Inc., 1976.

Becker, Howard S. *Outsiders: Studies in the Sociology of Deviance.* Glencoe, Ill.: Free Press, 1963.

Cammer, Leonard. *Freedom from Compulsion.* New York: Simon & Schuster, 1976.

Cooley, Charles W. *Social Organization; and Human Nature and the Social Order: The Two Major Works.* Glencoe, Ill.: Free Press, 1956.

Goldbeck, Nikki and David. *The Dieter's Companion: A Guide to Nutritional Self-Sufficiency.* New York: McGraw-Hill, 1975.

Jong, Erica. *Fear of Flying.* New York: Holt, Rinehart & Winston, 1973.

Laing, R. D. *The Politics of Experience.* New York: Pantheon Books, 1967.

Mead, George H. *Mind, Self and Society.* Chicago, Ill.: University of Chicago Press, 1934.

Morehouse, Laurence E., and Gross, Leonard. *Total Fitness in 30 Minutes a Week.* New York: Simon & Schuster, 1975.

Overeaters Anonymous: A Program of Recovery for Compulsive Overeaters. "Are You a Compulsive Overeater?" Los Angeles, Calif.: Overeaters Anonymous, World Services, 1973.

Osman, Jack D. *Thin from Within.* New York: Hart Publishing Co., 1976.